Practical Simulation of Radar Antennas and Radomes

The Artech House Antenna Library

Blake, L.V., **Antennas**

Freeman, Ernest R., **Interference Suppression Techniques for Microwave Antennas and Transmitters**

Hirsch, Herbert L., and Douglas C. Grove, **Practical Simulation of Radar Antennas and Radomes**

Jahoda, Joseph R., and L. Earl Mills, **Aircraft Antennas**

Keiser, Bernhard E., **Principles of Electromagnetic Compatibility**

Law, Preston E., Jr., **Shipboard Antennas**

Law, Preston E., Jr., **Shipboard Electromagnetics**

Li, S.T., J.C. Logan, J.W. Rockway, and D.W.S. Tam, **Microcomputer Tools for Communications Engineering**

Li, S.T., J.C. Logan, J.W. Rockway, and D.W.S. Tam, **The MININEC System: Microcomputer Analysis of Wire Antennas**

Pozar, David M., **Antenna Design Using Personal Computers**

Sletten, Carlyle J., ed., **Reflector and Lens Antennas: Analysis and Design Using Personal Computers**

Wolff, Edward A., **Antenna Analysis: Revised 2nd Edition**

Practical Simulation of Radar Antennas and Radomes

*Herbert L. Hirsch
and Douglas C. Grove*

Artech House

Library of Congress Cataloging-in-Publication Data

Hirsch, Herbert L.
    Practical simulation of radar antennas and radomes / Herbert L.
Hirsch, Douglas C. Grove.
        p.   cm.
    Bibliography: p.
    Includes index.
    ISBN 0-89006-237-4
    1. Radar—Antennas—Mathematical models. 2. Radar—Antennas—Com-
puter simulation. 3. Radomes—Mathematical models. 4. Radomes—Com-
puter simulation. I. Grove, Douglas C. II. Title.
    TK6590.A6H57   1988
    621.3848'3—dc19   87-35087

International Standard Book Number: 0-89006-237-4
Library of Congress Catalog Card Number: 87-35087

10 9 8 7 6 5 4 3 2 1

to Susan Diane

to the Folks

Contents

Preface

The value of this book is in providing accurate, yet computationally simple models for antennas and radomes. These models are highly desirable to systems engineers and simulation designers because they permit near real-time processing without the use of a specialized and often expensive high-speed processor. The trade-off in simulation design is always accuracy *versus* speed, and the rigorous simulation of these devices, based on electromagnetic field theory, is simply too slow for most practical applications.

So, because the simulation designer needs fast, accurate models, how can he or she acquire them? Obviously, one way is to develop them, but this requires in-depth knowledge and specialized skills in these particular fields. So, the designer must either hire or acquire these skills, and then undertake a development effort, which is both expensive and time-consuming. The authors know—we have been through it! This book, however, offers the results of these efforts on a "how to" basis, saving the reader considerable time and expense.

The book is divided into three parts: Part I is an introduction to simulation, Part II addresses antenna simulation, and Part III deals with radome simulation. Parts II and III of the book derive and demonstrate practical simulation techniques. However, they approach the techniques from somewhat opposite perspectives.

The two introductory chapters of Part I set the stage for the rest of the book. Here, we present a general overview that permits the simulation designer to see how the radar antenna and radome models interact with each other and with other components of a radar simulation. Also, we define the electromagnetic, mathematical, and geometric conventions used throughout the book.

Part II addresses the radar antenna simulation model. Chapter 3 presents a fairly detailed derivation of the fundamental algorithm for this model. The user should find this information valuable because a deeper understanding of a technique will generally foster a greater degree of confidence in it. Also, a skilled user may even find a way to improve a technique if he or she understands it well. Chapters 4 through 6 extend the basic algorithm from the general case to its specific use in modeling several particular antenna types. Although the algorithm gains complexity through this process, it still remains significantly more simple than the actual antenna functions which it simulates. In Chapter 7, the algorithm is further extended into the popular monopulse configurations that more or less dominate the tracking systems of today's technology. We give particular attention to the validity of the angular error function produced through the use of the algorithm. Sample cases abound throughout these chapters, giving the reader many specific examples of how to apply the several variations of the model.

The radome model is the subject of Part III. Chapter 8 discusses the geometric principles involved in radome transmission and the application of some creative simplifications to the radome geometry. Chapter 9 follows with a presentation of transmission and refraction principles applicable to the simplified geometry from the previous chapter. As in Part II, a thorough treatment of the model design is performed to give the reader a usable, working understanding. At this point, we establish the basic radome transmission and refraction algorithms, which are applied to some typical single-layer and multiple-layer radomes in Chapters 10 and 11. Through these chapters, several cases are presented and verified, thus giving the reader valid, specific examples from which to work.

The appendices offer all the modeling techniques and algorithms from Parts II and III as usable code. We structure the subroutines and drivers in a modular fashion and document them well to provide the user with ready-to-use models, which may be used as is or easily converted to other languages.

For the primary users—simulation designers and systems engineers—this book offers an alternative to antenna and radome design texts. Using the techniques and methods presented here, these individuals can create accurate, fast-processing models that can easily be fitted to

- functional requirements;
- manufacturers' data;
- measured data.

The art of simulation design is that of configuring models which are both functionally accurate and computationally simple. In balancing accuracy and simplicity, the designer may choose to group mathematical quantities and define terms in a manner which may appear somewhat unconventional to individuals who are familiar with the physical hardware being simulated. In this text, if we do take some license with popular conventions for mathematical convenience, we will explain the reason for the deviation so that the reader is comfortable with the presented technique.

Antenna and radome designers can use this book as a complement or supplement to design texts. These individuals will be able to perform requirement trade-offs and investigate many iterations very rapidly, using the modeling techniques presented here. Once the designers establish the requirements, they may conduct the actual design of the antenna or radome as they normally would.

The use of this text eliminates the necessity of understanding electromagnetic theory in great depth in order to develop models. The reader may simply apply the modeling techniques that are presented as usable code in the appendices. The reader need learn only how to apply the modeling functions properly to a particular requirement, which is accomplished by a step-by-step explanation of the basic functions and many practical examples. The book is not saying "This is how to design antennas and radomes." It is saying "Because there are such devices, this is how to simulate them." It is a user's manual for antenna and radome simulations.

We firmly believe in good engineering, but not in re-engineering. Once a problem is solved, the solution should be shared with others so that they need not solve the same problem again. The contents of this book are the results of our success in constructing accurate and useful models. We are confident that our colleagues will find them applicable to their simulation requirements without the wear and tear of a full-scale development. Good luck!

Herbert L. Hirsch
Douglas C. Grove

ACKNOWLEDGMENT

The authors would like to express their gratitude to Kurt E. Hildebrant for his expertise and assistance in the design of several utility routines, and to Hal Schrank for his valuable insight and advice.

PART I
INTRODUCTION TO RADAR SYSTEM SIMULATION

This book is for simulation engineers and designers. The book's purpose is to provide practical and straightforward techniques for mathematically modeling radar antennas and radomes.

The rapid growth of simulation in the past decade has created a need for converting hardware technology into software models. However, in the areas of microwave and radio frequency (RF), this conversion is often not easily accomplished. An RF design engineer can certainly produce the rigorous mathematical description of these devices. However, this description can be somewhat cumbersome, involving such mathematical tools as Fourier transforms, complex variables, and multiple surface integrations.

What about the simulation designer who needs a good model but has neither the time nor the budget to become an RF expert? He or she needs a good "cookbook" to produce usable software models, which are not only accurate, but also conserve the assets (processing time and memory space) that are every bit as precious to the simulation engineer as power and space are to the hardware designer.

This is precisely what this book is—a cookbook for radar antenna and radome simulation. Many excellent books are available that provide a thorough treatment of the physics and electromagnetic theories involved in these devices, but this is not one of them! This book concentrates on practical modeling techniques and relegates electromagnetic theory to a supporting role, in which it sets the stage for the models and confirms their utility and accuracy. This book does not bog us down in theory; rather, it leads us to the model that will solve our problem.

Chapter 1

Basic Electromagnetic Principles, Conventions, and Definitions

This chapter summarizes some relevant basic electromagnetic theory and outlines the geometric and mathematical conventions used throughout the remaining chapters. The reader who is well versed in vector mathematics or electromagnetic theory may wish to skip these sections because the terms and definitions are quite conventional. However, we recommend that all readers review the section pertaining to geometric conventions because a variety of reference systems are currently in use, and the one chosen for this text may not be the one with which the reader is acquainted.

We do not present the topics in this chapter in rigorous depth. Rather, they serve as a convenient reference and brief summary of the basics on which to base the simulation techniques in the text.

1.1 GEOMETRIC CONVENTIONS

The rectangular-coordinate reference system used throughout the book is illustrated in Figure 1.1. For antenna situations, the aperture of the antenna is considered to lie on the y-z plane, centered on the x-axis. In the case of radome situations, the base of the radome is also considered to lie on the y-z plane, but it may or may not be centered on the x-axis, depending on whether it is symmetrical.

The relationships among several geometric quantities are also shown in Figure 1.1. These are defined as follows:

Line of sight. A line connecting the center of the rectangular coordinate system and some point of interest, *S*.

Look vector. A unit vector lying on the line of sight.

Boresight. The direction in which a device (usually an antenna) is pointing. This is the *x*-axis in a local coordinate system which is steered with the device.

Look angle (θ). The angle between the look vector (or line of sight) and the boresight.

Elevation angle (θ_e). The angle between the look vector (or line of sight) and its projection on the *x-y* plane of the local coordinate system. (This angle is often called the *elevation component* of the look angle.)

Azimuth angle (θ_a). The angle between the projection of the look vector (or line of sight) on the *x-y* plane and the boresight. (This angle is often called the *azimuth component* of the look angle.)

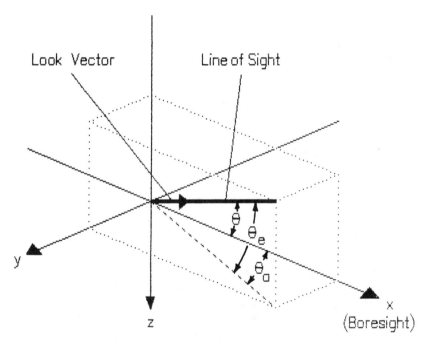

Figure 1.1 Geometric Reference System and Definitions

The geometric conventions used for radiation incident on and transmitted through a surface or boundary are shown in Figure 1.2. These conventions are in accordance with classical physical and optical relationships.

The following definitions apply to the directions and angles of incidence, reflection, and refraction as shown in Figure 1.2.

Incidence angle (θ_i). The angle between the line of sight from a source S to the point of incidence P, and a vector normal to the surface or boundary at this point.

Reflection angle (θ_r). The angle between a vector along the direction of reflection and a vector normal to the surface or boundary at the point of incidence.

Refraction angle (θ_t). The angle between a vector along the direction of refraction and a vector normal to the surface or boundary at the point of incidence.

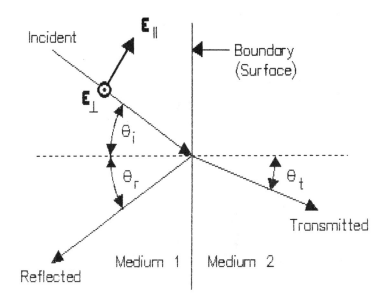

Figure 1.2 Boundary Relationships

Figure 1.2 also illustrates the components of a vector, **E**, which are parallel and perpendicular to the plane of incidence, a plane defined by the line of sight and a vector normal to the surface. In electromagnetic applications, the magnitude of this vector would represent the electric field strength and its direction would relate to polarization. These topics are discussed further in Section 1.3, but it is convenient to illustrate the concept of parallel and perpendicular (tangential and normal) components here.

1.2 VECTOR MATHEMATICS

Vector mathematics are used quite commonly in electromagnetic applications. Although this book strives to reduce all mathematics to the least possible complexity, some vector relationships are used in derivations and explanations. Therefore, we present a review of the basics to provide sufficient background to understand the concepts developed in the following chapters.

Figure 1.3 illustrates an example of a vector in a rectangular coordinate system. The vector has not only magnitude, as a scalar quantity would, but also direction. Vector quantities are designated as variables printed in **boldface** type, as Figure 1.3 shows.

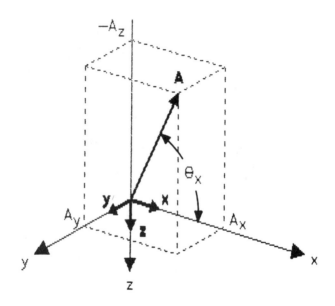

Figure 1.3 Vector Components in the Reference System

The vector of Figure 1.3, or any vector in a rectangular coordinate system for that matter, may be expressed as the sum of its components along the three coordinate axes:

$$\mathbf{A} = A_x\mathbf{x} + A_y\mathbf{y} + A_z\mathbf{z} \tag{1.1}$$

where

A_x, A_y, A_z = the magnitudes of the three components

$\mathbf{x}, \mathbf{y}, \mathbf{z}$ = unit vectors along the three axes

An important concept in electromagnetic theory is that of the *direction cosine*. A direction cosine for a particular coordinate axis is simply the cosine of the angle between the vector and that axis. For example, the direction cosine for the x-axis of Figure 1.3 may be expressed as

$$a = \cos\theta_x = A_x/|\mathbf{A}| \tag{1.2}$$

where $a =$ the x-axis direction cosine of $\mathbf{A}$. The same concept is true for direction cosines for the y and z axes.

In similar fashion to the vector $\mathbf{A}$, another vector, $\mathbf{B}$, may be defined as

$$\mathbf{B} = B_x\mathbf{x} + B_y\mathbf{y} + B_z\mathbf{z}$$

The sum of the two vectors $\mathbf{A}$ and $\mathbf{B}$ may be written as the sum of their components along the three coordinate axes:

$$\mathbf{A} + \mathbf{B} = (A_x + B_x)\mathbf{x} + (A_y + B_y)\mathbf{y} + (A_z + B_z)\mathbf{z} \tag{1.3}$$

The product of a vector and a scalar is simply a vector of the same direction with a magnitude equal to the product of its original magnitude and the multiplying scalar:

$$K\mathbf{A} = KA\mathbf{a} \tag{1.4}$$

where

$\mathbf{A} = A\mathbf{a}$ (a vector)
$K =$ a multiplying scalar

Two important mathematical operations in vector mathematics involve the product of two vectors. These are the *dot product* and the *cross product*. Figure 1.4 illustrates the vector relationships pertaining to these operations. The vectors $\mathbf{A}$ and $\mathbf{B}$ lie in a plane, and the unit vector $\mathbf{c}$ is perpendicular to that plane.

The dot product, sometimes called the scalar product, is a scalar quantity and may be expressed as

$$\mathbf{A} \cdot \mathbf{B} = AB \cos\alpha$$
$$\mathbf{A} \cdot \mathbf{B} = A_xB_x + A_yB_y + A_zB_z \tag{1.5}$$

Notice that because the dot product is a scalar, it is mathematically commutative:

$$\mathbf{A} \cdot \mathbf{B} = \mathbf{B} \cdot \mathbf{A}$$

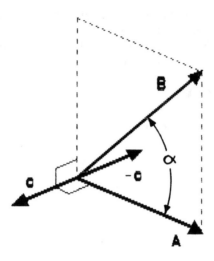

Figure 1.4 Two Co-Planar Vectors

The cross product, sometimes called the vector product, is a vector quantity and is expressed as

$$\mathbf{A} \times \mathbf{B} = (AB \sin\alpha)\mathbf{c}$$

$$\mathbf{A} \times \mathbf{B} = \begin{vmatrix} A_x & A_y & A_z \\ B_x & B_y & B_z \\ \mathbf{x} & \mathbf{y} & \mathbf{z} \end{vmatrix}$$

$$\mathbf{A} \times \mathbf{B} = (A_y B_z - A_z B_y)\mathbf{x} + (A_z B_x - A_x B_z)\mathbf{y}$$
$$+ (A_x B_y - A_y B_x)\mathbf{z} \tag{1.6}$$

Because the cross product is a vector quantity, it is not commutative. The cross product $\mathbf{B} \times \mathbf{A}$ would have the same magnitude but the opposite direction as the cross product $\mathbf{A} \times \mathbf{B}$. This can be expressed as

$$\mathbf{B} \times \mathbf{A} = (AB \sin\alpha)(-\mathbf{c})$$

These vector products may now be used to define some additional vector operations. First, the differential operator, del ($\vec{\nabla}$), is defined as follows:

$$\vec{\nabla} = \frac{\partial}{\partial_x}\mathbf{x} + \frac{\partial}{\partial_y}\mathbf{y} + \frac{\partial}{\partial_z}\mathbf{z}$$

The gradient is defined as the vector differential operator applied to a scalar function:

$$F = \text{grad } F = \frac{\partial_F}{\partial_x}\mathbf{x} + \frac{\partial_F}{\partial_y}\mathbf{y} + \frac{\partial_F}{\partial_z}\mathbf{z} \qquad (1.7)$$

where F = a scalar function of x,y,z.

The divergence of a vector is the dot product of the differential operator and the vector:

$$\vec{\nabla}\cdot\mathbf{A} = \text{div } \mathbf{A} \text{ (the divergence)} \qquad (1.8)$$

where $\mathbf{A}$ is a vector.

The curl of a vector is defined as the cross product of the differential operator and the vector:

$$\vec{\nabla}\times\mathbf{A} = \text{curl } \mathbf{A} \text{ (the curl)} \qquad (1.9)$$

where $\mathbf{A}$ is a vector.

This concludes the overview of vector mathematics. The concepts presented here, although not very rigorous, are sufficient for the purpose of this text.

1.3   ELECTROMAGNETIC THEORY

The fundamental electromagnetic theory concepts pertinent to this text are those of the electric field intensity, and how this quantity relates to polarization. The electric field intensity is a vector quantity and is quantified as volts per linear measure, usually volts per meter.

Figure 1.5 shows a uniform, sinusoidal plane wave traveling along the x-axis of a rectangular coordinate system.

The electric field intensity E may be expressed as

$$\tilde{E} = \mathbf{E}e^{j(\omega t + \phi)}$$
$$\tilde{E} = \mathbf{E}\angle\phi \text{ (phasor notation)} \qquad (1.10)$$

where
$\quad\quad$ $\mathbf{E}$ = peak magnitude vector
$\quad\quad$ ϕ = phase shift
$\quad\quad$ ω = $2\pi f$ (f is the frequency)

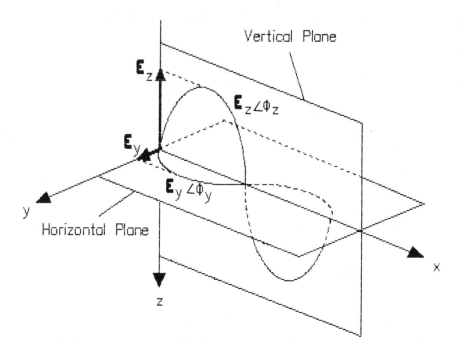

Figure 1.5 Polarization Components of a Traveling Wave

The phasor notation offers a simplified form that expresses only the peak magnitude and phase shift.

The magnitude and direction of the electric field intensity vector for the traveling wave will vary with time. Polarization of this quantity is simply a means of expressing the geometric shape bounding the end point of the electric field intensity vector.

We can easily visualize this concept by imagining the traveling wave traversing a plane parallel to the y-z plane (perpendicular to the direction of travel). This plane is referred to as the *polarization plane*. The geometric shape, traced on the plane by the end point of the electric field intensity vector over one complete cycle, describes the nature of the polarization.

The traveling wave shown in Figure 1.5 has a component in the x-y plane and the x-z plane. The nature of the polarization is a function of the amplitude and phase relationships between these components. Figure 1.6 illustrates the possible variations.

When the magnitude of **E** exists only in one plane, the polarization is said to be *linear*. For instance, if E_z is present and E_y is zero, the wave is said to have vertical linear polarization. Conversely, when E_y is present and E_z is zero, horizontal linear polarization exists. If both E_y and E_z are present and the two

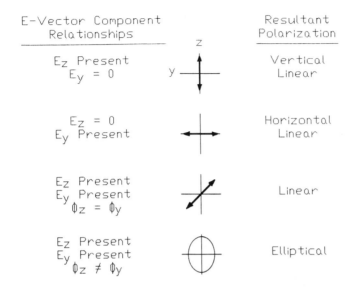

Figure 1.6 Polarization Variations

components in each plane are in phase ($\phi_y = \phi_z$), the polarization is still linear, but not along either coordinate axis. In all these cases, the shape traced on the polarization plane is a straight line. Hence, we have the name, linear polarization.

If the amplitudes of the two components differ, or they are out of phase with each other, or both, then the shape traced on the polarization plane by the traveling wave is that of an ellipse. Thus, for these conditions the polarization is said to be *elliptical*.

A special case of elliptical polarization occurs when the amplitudes of the two components are equal and they are precisely 90° out of phase. This condition results in a circle being traced on the polarization plane and is consequently known as *circular polarization*.

The concept of polarization is important to both radomes and antennas because these devices have different responses to waves of different polarizations.

1.4 SUMMARY

This chapter presented some fundamental concepts and descriptions, which are used throughout the book as a concise and handy reference. In the course of using this text, the reader may find it useful to review some of this information from time to time.

The next chapter begins to apply these fundamentals to the task of modeling antennas and radomes.

Chapter 2

Radar System Component Interaction

Successful simulation of any type of system requires an appreciation of how the components of the system interact, as well as how the system functions in some environment of interest. In this case, the system under consideration is a radar system and the environment of interest is the electromagnetic environment around the radar system.

This chapter presents a generic overview of a radar simulation. Its purpose is to acquaint the reader with radar system components and how models of these components typically fit into a simulation involving both the radar system and the environment. We emphasize the interaction among the antenna and radome components and other system and environment components. This approach is designed to illustrate how the antenna and radome models developed in later chapters may be used in a wide variety of practical modeling applications.

2.1 COMPONENTS OF A RADAR SIMULATION

As previously mentioned, a radar simulation may be divided into two parts: the radar system and the environment. Therefore, a functional diagram of a radar simulation would simply consist of these two functions, as shown in Figure 2.1.

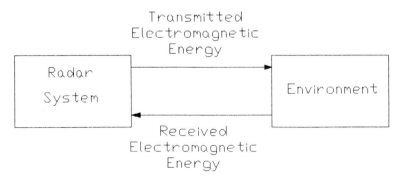

Figure 2.1 Basic Radar Simulation Functional Diagram

At this level of functionality, the linkage between the two parts of the simulation need not be quantified in great detail, and may be described simply as transmission and reception at some frequency.

The radar system portion of the simulation may be further divided into components as shown in Table 2.1.

Table 2.1

Radar System Components

Electromechanical System
Electronic System
Antenna or Antenna System
Radome

The division of the radar system into functional components at this level has not disturbed the generic quality of the functional description. A particular radar system will usually have all the components listed in Table 2.1. The specific definition of the functions of these components converts this functional description to that of a particular type of radar.

Similarly, the environment portion of the simulation may be divided into the components listed in Table 2.2. Again, this division of the environment into functional components has left the functional description at a generic level.

Table 2.2

Radar Environment Components

Range Propagation
Reflectors
Emitters

The functional diagram of Figure 2.1 may be modified to include the level of detail defined by the functional divisions of Tables 2.1 and 2.2. We present this modified functional diagram in Figure 2.2. At this point, it is important to understand these functions and the information that moves among them.

We can best describe the components of the functional diagram of Figure 2.2 and their interactions by following the process of a single radar cycle. For these discussions, a cycle will be considered to consist of transmission, reflection, and reception, without particular concern for either the timing implications or the specific purpose of the radar.

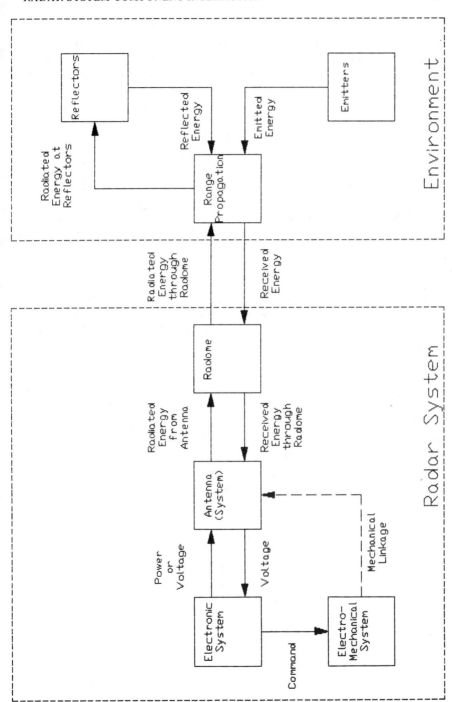

Figure 2.2 Components of a Radar Simulation

To begin the cycle, the electronic system must deliver some electromagnetic energy to the antenna. This energy may be described as an actual voltage developed across the terminal impedance of the antenna, or more simply as the power delivered to the antenna.

The antenna in transmitting mode performs the function of emitting the electromagnetic energy into the atmosphere. If the antenna were a perfect isotropic radiator, it would simply transfer the energy to the atmosphere in a uniform, spherical distribution. However, a radar antenna is much more specialized and sophisticated than this idealization. The antenna has a particular three-dimensional radiation pattern, which serves to focus or direct the electromagnetic energy into a particular form to perform a specific radar function. The specific radar functions are diverse and varied, and the antennas required to perform some of them are equally diverse and may actually be systems of antennas rather than individual antennas.

Regardless of the specific nature of the antenna or antenna system, its radiation pattern may be described as either a power gain or voltage gain as a function of the azimuth and elevation angles with respect to the boresight (or pointing axis) of the antenna. The gain represents the ratio of power density (power gain) or electric field intensity (voltage gain) delivered from the antenna to that of an isotropic radiator, at a particular azimuth and elevation angle combination.

Electromagnetic energy emitted from the antenna must then pass through a *radome*: a protective cover for the antenna that shields it from environmental elements. Like the antenna, the radome is designed to support the specific function of the radar system. However, the radome must also be physically compatible with the radar antenna's mounting apparatus, which can lead to design compromises between electromagnetic performance and physical requirements. Any airborne radar system exemplifies this compromise because a radome, the shape of which is dictated by aerodynamic design, is not necessarily optimized for electromagnetic performance.

The size, shape, and composition of the radome dictate its performance characteristics. These may be quantified in terms of a transmission coefficient and an angular refraction associated with the geometric optical characteristics and electromagnetic properties of the layers of the radome.

Once transmitted through the radome, the electromagnetic energy propagates through the environment. Unless the radar is operating over an extremely long range, such as with a satellite-tracking application, or through rain, we usually ignore transmission effects of the atmosphere. Because the emission is corrected for radome effects within the radome component and related to the isotropic case by the antenna gain, the propagation may be considered isotropic. Thus, the power density at any range from the antenna is proportional to the inverse of the square of the range. Similarly, the electric field intensity is proportional to the inverse of the range.

At this point, the radar situation and its simulation can become quite complicated. In addition to the target of interest to the radar system, we must consider many other reflectors, including vehicles, buildings, and terrain. The electromagnetic energy intercepted by a reflective object will return an amount of reflected energy proportional to two physical properties: area and reflectivity. The object's reflectivity (a function of its geometric and physical properties) may be complex, which will cause the reflected energy to have a different polarization than that of the transmitted energy. Also, the reflecting object may consist of several types of materials, each having different physical properties and different areas. Any object with physical size will reflect a radar emission, and so the modeler must use considerable discretion in defining which objects should be modeled, and to what accuracy, for a given application. Also, the modeler may have to consider emitters, which will introduce direct emissions into the radar in addition to the reflected ones. The point of this discussion is that for a single transmitted radar transmission, we may have to deal with several return emissions.

The electromagnetic energy from reflectors and emitters then propagates back to be received by the radar system. This received energy is transmitted through the radome. In similar fashion to the transmitting path, the effects of the radome consist of a transmissive loss and an angular refraction.

Electromagnetic energy passes through the radome, then enters the antenna or antenna system and is subject to its gain characteristic. The output of the antenna is a voltage developed across its terminal impedance, which is delivered to the electronic system.

The electronic system then applies whatever signal processing techniques are necessary to perform its specialized function. These techniques involve discrimination of the temporal, frequency, and phase characteristics as well as the amplitude of the voltage signal presented to this system. Often, especially when the radar is used to track a moving target, the electronic system will deliver a command to an electromechanical system, which will physically point the antenna in a new direction.

From these discussions, we may conclude that the principal effect of the antenna system is gain, while the principal effects of the radome consist of transmissive losses and refraction. This statement, although overly simplified at this point, is true. We begin a more detailed assessment of antenna and radome effects in the next section, which lays the groundwork for the models developed in the later chapters. Because antennas and radomes are the subject of this book, the remaining radar systems and environmental components are not discussed further in any significant detail.

2.2 INTERACTION AMONG RADAR SYSTEM AND ENVIRONMENTAL COMPONENTS

In spite of the diversity of input and output requirements in various modeling applications, we may describe antenna and radome components by functional models that are common to both the transmitting and receiving modes. These common functional models are developed into complete and useful simulations in the remaining chapters of this book.

2.2.1 The Antenna Functional Model

As discussed in the previous section, in the transmitting path, the antenna converts power or voltage across its input into electromagnetic energy, which radiates into the environment. The radiated energy is typically quantified as transmitted power for simple simulations, or as the transmitted electric field intensity for applications concerned with phase and polarization effects. Thus, a simulation of the antenna in the transmitting mode must have some provision for handling the appropriate parametric conversions. Also, an antenna model may need to account for losses due to impedance mismatch and dissipated heat. All things considered, a functional diagram of an antenna in the transmitting path is shown in Figure 2.3.

We may quantify these functions through some elementary network analysis. A portion of the antenna functional diagram may be considered a network, as illustrated in Figure 2.4. In this network, the input terminal impedance is considered to consist of two series impedances, one representing losses, Z_l, and the other representing the ideal or lossless antenna impedance, Z_a. The voltage and power gains are each separated into two orthogonal polarization components. G_{vc} and G_{pc} are the co-polarized voltage and power gains, respectively, while G_{vx} and G_{px} represent their cross-polarized counterparts. These gains are all considered to be multiplicative amplification factors. The output impedance, Z_0.

The reader should note that the subscript x used in Figure 2.4 and throughout the book represents a cross-polarized component of some variable and *not* a component in the x-axis of the coordinate system.

The loss compensation is handled by defining a composite loss impedance, Z_l, across which all losses within the antenna are considered to occur. By isolating these losses in this fashion, we may consider the remainder of the network ideal or lossless, and thus simplify its analysis. Because both the power and voltage across two series impedances will divide proportionately to these impedances, the loss-compensated power or voltage may be related to the input power or voltage:

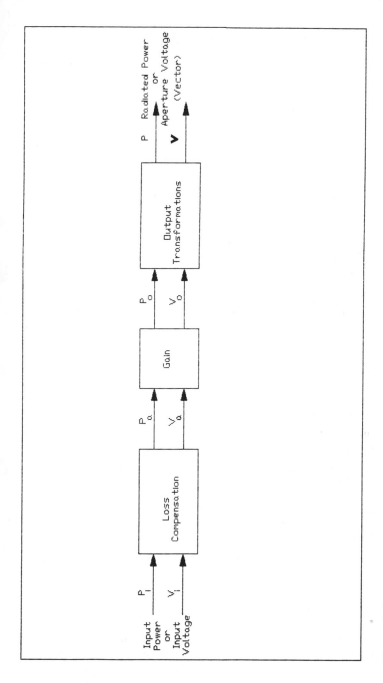

Figure 2.3 Transmitting Path Antenna Model

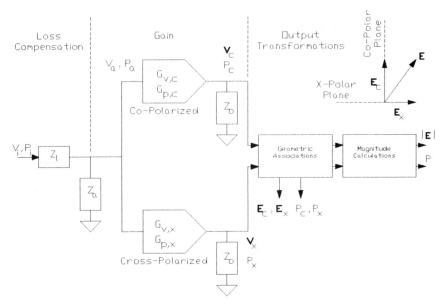

Figure 2.4 Network Representation of the Transmitting Path Antenna Functional Diagram

$$P_a = P_i - P_l \tag{2.1}$$
$$V_a = V_i - V_l \tag{2.2}$$

where

P_i = input power
P_l = loss power
P_a = loss-compensated power
V_i = input voltage
V_l = loss voltage
V_a = loss-compensated voltage

Moving terms, we may rewrite (2.1) and (2.2) in the following manner:

$$P_a = (1 - P_l/P_i)P_i \tag{2.3}$$
$$V_a = (1 - V_l/V_i)V_i \tag{2.4}$$

The coefficients of the input power and input voltage in (2.3) and (2.4) are mathematically equal. They are equal because the same input current is present in the loss impedance and the rest of the network. Therefore, the input and loss powers may be expressed in terms of their voltages as follows:

$$P_l = V_l I$$
$$P_i = V_i I$$

where I is the input current.

The coefficients from (2.3) and (2.4) are thus shown to be equivalent, and are expressed as an efficiency coefficient:

$$1 - P_l/P_i = 1 - V_l I/V_i I = 1 - V_l/V_i = K_e$$

where K_e is the efficiency coefficient.

The efficiency is a simple and popular means for adjusting either the input power or the input voltage for composite losses. Because the losses may be both resistive and reactive, we would have to do some complex calculations to arrive at the loss-compensated power and voltage. However, in practice, the efficiency is usually given as a fraction or percentage of the input, which we use directly to calculate these quantities:

$$P_a = P_i K_e \tag{2.5}$$
$$V_a = V_i K_e \tag{2.6}$$

where K_e is the fractional efficiency.

Note that in some cases, the losses are already considered in the given voltage gain or power gain of an antenna. In these cases, the input power and voltage may be considered already loss-compensated. In other words, the efficiency term of (2.5) and (2.6) is set to 100% or 1.0, which effectively eliminates the loss impedance of Figure 2.4 and makes the loss-compensated power or voltage equal to the input power or voltage.

In a typical simulation, the calculation of antenna gain will produce the radiated power density or electric field intensity at some point of interest as a function of input power or voltage, and look angle. However, because the calculations of these quantities involve the range or distance to the point of interest, it is convenient to deal only with the gain in the antenna portion of a simulation and to introduce the range effects in a separate range propagation portion. This is simply good, structured programming technique.

By segregating the simulation in this fashion, the output of the antenna portion becomes radiated power, or a quantity that mathematically has the dimension of "volts" but no physical meaning in terms of a voltage output of an antenna. For the purpose of this text, we define this quantity as the *aperture voltage* of the antenna.

The reader who is experienced with RF principles and antenna design from a systems or hardware perspective may find this aperture voltage concept somewhat unconventional, especially because antennas are power transfer devices in the first place. However, we have two very good reasons for using this particular concept.

First, in many simulations of this nature, the electric field intensity vector is the quantity that is tracked through the various components of the simulation. The nature of the aperture voltage is such that we can calculate the magnitude of the electric field at any range simply by dividing the aperture voltage by the product of the range and a constant. This process is considerably less complicated than carrying the radiated power and calculating the electric field magnitude from it, especially in applications involving many reflections and emissions. This principle is clearly demonstrated through the mathematical derivations presented later in this section.

Second, the mathematical models producing the gain for a particular antenna operate more conveniently and with less computational complexity in the voltage domain rather than the power domain. This will become apparent when the various models are developed and demonstrated in Chapters 3, 4, 5, and 6. Once we determine a voltage gain, we can quite easily obtain the corresponding power gain simply by squaring the voltage gain.

Although the power and voltage gain transformations often seem quite complicated, these processes are simplified considerably if we pay attention to a fundamental physical principle: conservation of energy.

Because losses are accounted for by the previously described loss-compensation process, the output energy from an antenna must equal the input energy. Also, because energy is the product of power and time, for a simultaneous process such as this, the output power must equal the input power. In other words,

$$\text{Energy In} = \text{Energy Out}$$
$$(\text{Power} \times \text{Time}) \text{ In} = (\text{Power} \times \text{Time}) \text{ Out}$$

However,

$$\text{Time In} = \text{Time Out}$$

so

$$\text{Power In} = \text{Power Out}$$

The power and voltage gain of the antenna may seem to violate this principle, but this is not actually so. Remember that the gain of an antenna represents the focusing of its radiated energy into a narrow, solid angle. Thus, at some given look angle, the antenna may appear to be creating energy with an enormous gain, but this is compensated by losses at other look angles. The net effect over the entire sphere of possible radiation is that the radiated power is equal to the input power minus the power losses.

This principle may be applied to the gain portion of Figure 2.4. For now, we will ignore the fact that two individual gain calculations must be made for the two polarization planes. The calculations are identical in both cases and may be more conveniently derived through the generic representation of Figure 2.5.

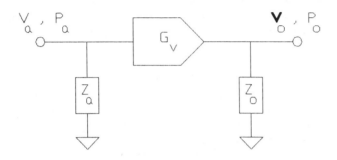

Figure 2.5 Generic Voltage Gain Network for the Transmitting Path

Mathematically, the conservation of energy, or power in this case, may be written as

$$P_0 = P_a \tag{2.7}$$

where

P_0 = total radiated output power

P_a = input power to the gain function of Figure 2.5

Because power is defined as the square of voltage divided by impedance, we may write (2.7) as

$$\frac{V_0^2}{Z_0} = \frac{V_a^2}{Z_a} \tag{2.7a}$$

where

V_a = input voltage to the gain function of Figure 2.5

Z_a = antenna input impedance

V_0 = aperture voltage

Z_0 = impedance of free space

Then, after rearranging terms and solving for the output voltage, we can calculate the previously described aperture voltage:

$$V_0 = V_a(Z_0/Z_a)^{1/2} \tag{2.8}$$

By inserting the voltage gain term G_v as a coefficient of the right side of (2.8), we convert this equation from a total power expression to that of a focused or directed power at the look angle corresponding to the particular gain. Following a simple progression of exchanging variables, we derive four equations that express all possible combinations of input and output conditions. These equations are summarized in Table 2.3.

Table 2.3

Input	Output	Equation
Voltage	Aperture Voltage	(2.9)
Power	Aperture Voltage	(2.10)
Voltage	Radiated Power	(2.11)
Power	Radiated Power	(2.12)

The equations are written as follows:

$$V_0 = G_v(Z_0)^{1/2}V_a/(Z_a)^{1/2} \tag{2.9}$$

$$V_0 = G_v(Z_0)^{1/2}(P_a)^{1/2} \tag{2.10}$$

$$P_0 = V_0^2/Z_0 = G_v^2V_a^2/Z_a \tag{2.11}$$

$$P_0 = G_v^2P_a \tag{2.12}$$

These equations highlight two important facts. The first is that the power gain is simply the square of the voltage gain. The second is that all possible cases of gain for the transmitting path may be expressed mathematically as a function of the voltage gain.

The generic case discussed above is applicable to both polarization planes. The gain associated with the principal polarization plane is often referred to as the *co-polarized gain*. Because the plane of polarization orthogonal to the principal polarization plane crosses it at a 90° angle, the gain in this plane is referred to as the *cross-polarized gain*.

When the co-polarized gain is used in (2.9), (2.10), (2.11), or (2.12), the calculated quantities are the following:

V_c = co-polarized aperture voltage
P_c = co-polarized radiated power

Similarly, when the cross-polarized gain is used in these equations, the results are

V_x = cross-polarized aperture voltage
P_x = cross-polarized radiated power

The purpose of the output transformations is to resolve the co-polarized and cross-polarized aperture voltages and radiated powers into forms that are compatible with the total simulation. This typically involves the association of these quantities with some geometric reference system and the calculation of their resultant magnitudes.

In a simulation in which we fairly rigorously represent reflectors and emitters the quantity at the reflecting surface in which we are interested is the electric field intensity, which is a vector quantity. If the aperture voltage can be represented by a vector quantity, then the resulting electric field intensity at some range may be calculated as follows:

$$\mathbf{E} = \mathbf{V}_0/(4\pi)^{1/2}R \tag{2.13}$$

where
$\mathbf{E}$ = electric field intensity at some range, R
$\mathbf{V}_0$ = aperture voltage expressed as a vector quantity
R = range

The aperture voltage vector quantity $\mathbf{V}_0$ is simply the resultant vector of two vectors, the magnitudes of which are the aperture voltages calculated for the two polarization planes, and the directions of which are perpendicular to the line-of-sight vector between the antenna and the reflector and in the polarization planes. This situation and the relationship between aperture voltage and electric field intensity are shown graphically in Figure 2.6.

Once we have determined the two vector components of the electric field intensity, $\mathbf{E}_c$ and $\mathbf{E}_x$, or their resultant, $\mathbf{E}$, it may be necessary to transform them into the basic geometric reference system of the simulation. We have a wide variety of reference system conventions and transformation techniques—in fact, too many to address here. It suffices to say that some additional geometric transformations will most likely be necessary.

If we wish to know specific polarization, it is much more practical to carry the electric field intensity vector through the range calculations and geometric transformations. However, in the case of less rigorous simulations which are

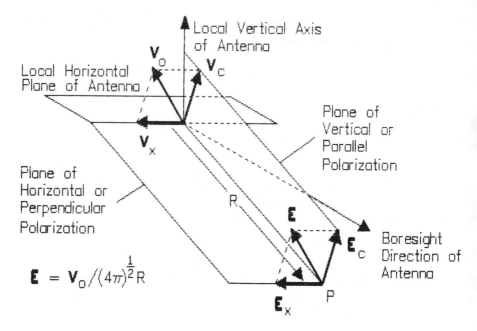

Figure 2.6 Electric Field Intensity and Aperture Voltage Relationships

concerned only with the radiated power, we are usually concerned with only the magnitude of the resultant power from the co-polarized and cross-polarized power components. In fact, simplistic simulations often ignore entirely the cross-polarized component in the transmitting path because its magnitude is usually considerably less than that of the co-polarized component. In any case, the resultant power may be calculated as follows:

$$P_0 = P_c + P_x \tag{2.14}$$

where

P_0 = resultant radiated power
P_c = co-polarized power
P_x = cross-polarized power

Therefore, the power density at some point of interest, such as a reflecting surface or receiving antenna, may be calculated as

$$P_d = P_0/4\pi R^2 \tag{2.15}$$

where

P_d = power density at some range

R = range

P_0 = radiated power

The antenna simulation in the receiving path has several functional components that are identical to those used in the transmitting path. Figure 2.7 shows the functional diagram for this case. In this situation, the input to the antenna function consists of several power densities or electric field intensities, which represent the returns from an assortment of reflectors and emitters. The output is typically a voltage or power developed across the terminal impedance of the antenna.

As in the receiving path situation, we can clarify the analysis by representing a portion of the functional diagram as an electrical network. Figure 2.8 shows the functional diagram for the receiving path with some additional network elements.

The electromagnetic energy incident on the antenna is usually expressed as either a power density or an electric field intensity. If we wish to process these quantities by the gain function of the antenna, we must convert them into the power or aperture voltage received by the antenna and then separate the co-polarized and cross-polarized components.

The total power received by the antenna may be expressed as

$$P_t = P_d(G_p\lambda^2/4\pi)$$

where

P_t = power received by the antenna

P_d = incident power density

G_p = antenna power gain

λ = wavelength

$G_p\lambda^2/4\pi$ = effective area of the antenna aperture

In structuring the simulation in the modular fashion shown in Figure 2.7 and Figure 2.8, it is desirable to isolate the constants in the effective area expression from the gain term, which will vary as a function of look angle and polarization. To isolate the constants, we define an intermediate power quantity P_i as the unity-gain received power, which we express as

$$P_i = P_d(\lambda^2/4\pi) \tag{2.16}$$

where P_i is the unity-gain received power.

Similarly, a unity-gain aperture voltage may be defined in this manner:

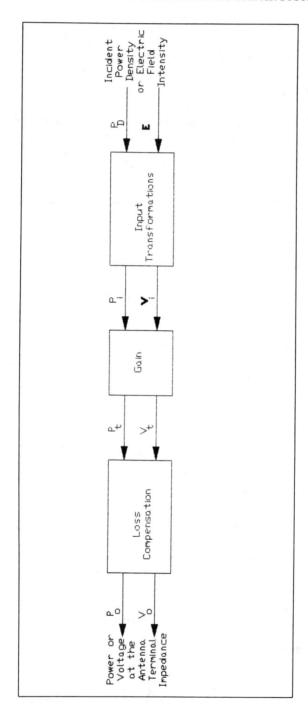

Figure 2.7 Receiving Path Antenna Model

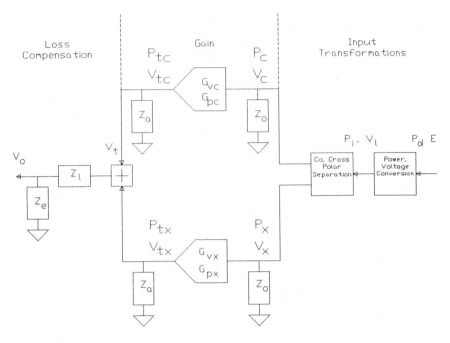

Figure 2.8 Network Representation of the Receiving Path Antenna Functional
Diagram

$$V_i = E|\lambda/(4\pi)^{1/2}| \tag{2.17}$$

where

V_i = unity-gain aperture voltage
E = incident electric field intensity

The appropriate multiplication by the power gain or voltage gain takes place
in the gain functions illustrated in Figure 2.8. Because the mathematical conversion of (2.17) is a scalar function, the conversion has no impact on the orientation
of the vector quantity E. Therefore, V_i has the same orientation as E.

The process of separating the co-polarized and cross-polarized components
involves the geometric transformation of V_i from the simulation reference system
to the antenna reference system, followed by the isolation of the components of
V_i in the two polarization planes and perpendicular to the line-of-sight vector
from the reflecting or emitting source to the antenna. Again, we will not present
specific discussions of the geometric transformations because the reference system conventions for different simulations can be quite diverse. At this point, the

outputs of interest are the magnitudes of the co-polarized and cross-polarized components of the aperture voltage.

For the case of a less rigorous simulation, which uses the power density, we typically consider reflected returns to be co-polarized. Cross-polarized power densities are usually attributed to emitters that are known to be polarized orthogonally to the receiving antenna. Therefore, rather than a geometric transformation, the process is simply that of designating the received power as either co-polarized or cross-polarized for each individual emitter or reflector return.

The results of these conversions and polarization component isolations are the following:

V_c = co-polarized aperture voltage
V_x = cross-polarized aperture voltage
P_c = co-polarized received power
P_x = cross-polarized received power

The gain function in the receiving path involves applying the appropriate voltage gain or power gain to the aperture voltage or power. As with the transmitting path situation, the gain function is computationally identical for both polarizations, differing only in the actual gain value for each polarization. The generic network diagram of Figure 2.9 is representative of either polarization, and it serves as a basis for deriving the gain expressions.

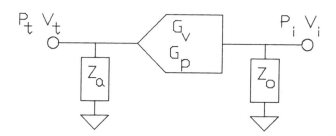

Figure 2.9 Generic Gain Network for the Receiving Path

Again, the principle of power conservation applies across the antenna. Therefore, for a power gain of unity and a lossless antenna, the input power must equal the output power:

$$P_t = P_i \qquad\qquad\qquad (2.18)$$

where

P_t = output power at the terminal impedance of the antenna

P_i = power received by the antenna

The input-output power equivalency of (2.18) may be written in terms of input and output voltages and impedances. This results in the following expression:

$$\frac{V_t^2}{Z_a} = \frac{V_i^2}{Z_0} \qquad (2.19)$$

where

V_t = voltage across the antenna terminal impedance

Z_a = antenna terminal impedance

V_i = aperture voltage

Z_0 = impedance of free space

If we then rearrange terms and insert the directive voltage gain at some look angle, we obtain an expression for terminal voltage as a function of aperture voltage:

$$V_t = G_v V_i (Z_a/Z_0)^{1/2} \qquad (2.20)$$

where G_v represents the antenna voltage gain.

Next, the aperture power may be expressed in terms of the aperture voltage and the impedance of free space:

$$P_i = V_i^2/Z_0 \qquad (2.21)$$

Substitution of (2.21) into (2.20) results in the expression of output voltage as a function of aperture power:

$$V_t = G_v (P_i)^{1/2} (Z_a)^{1/2} \qquad (2.22)$$

The application of (2.20) or (2.22) to the co-polarized and cross-polarized aperture voltage or power, using the appropriate gain for each polarization, results in the proper calculation of the two output voltages for the two polarizations. The composite output voltage across the antenna terminal impedance is the sum of these voltages and those representing each emitter and reflector contributing received electromagnetic energy to the antenna aperture. Because the phase of each voltage is a function of the range from the reflecting or emitting source, the addition of these voltages must be a phasor sum:

$$V\angle_{\phi_t} = \sum_{i=1}^{N}(V\angle_{\phi_{ci}} + V\angle_{\phi_{xi}})$$

(2.23)

where

V_t = composite terminal voltage

ϕ_t = composite terminal phase

V_{ci} = co-polarized terminal voltage of the ith source

ϕ_{ci} = co-polarized phase of the ith source

V_{xi} = cross-polarized terminal voltage of the ith source

ϕ_{xi} = cross-polarized phase of the ith source

N = number of sources

However, in the case of simple simulations concerned only with aggregate effects, we often ignore phase and perform a simple algebraic sum. In general, this type of simulation is concerned only with the relative amplitudes of the co-polarized and cross-polarized components, and not with the complex signal characteristics.

As a final step, we account for the losses of the antenna system by considering these losses to occur across an impedance representing the total combined losses. We do this in a way similar to that of the transmitting path— simply by multiplying the voltage across the terminal impedance by an efficiency coefficient:

$$V_0 = V_t K_e$$

(2.24)

where

K_e = fractional efficiency

V_t = either a vector or scalar quantity, depending on its use in the simulation

We thus conclude the functional description of the mathematical processes involved in the antenna gain functions for both the transmitting and receiving paths in a radar simulation. Throughout this description, we applied mathematics to a very rigorous simulation as well as to a simple model. Most simulations will fall somewhere within these extremes and the level of detail required will be a function of the intended use of the entire simulation.

It is important to note that both the transmitting and receiving cases employ a common element: the voltage gain or power gain module, which is a function of the azimuth and elevation angles between the antenna boresight vector and the line-of-sight vector from the antenna to a point of interest. Therefore, a practical, accurate, and functionally simple model, which can simulate the voltage gain and power gain of any antenna in either polarization plane, is the critical element to a successful antenna simulation. Just such a model is developed in Part II of this book.

2.2.2 The Radome Functional Model

The radome function is somewhat less complicated than that of the antenna. Its purpose is to apply the appropriate transmission and refraction effects to the electromagnetic energy passing through it.

Figure 2.10 illustrates the functional diagram of a typical radome function in the transmitting path. For this situation, the inputs are the vector representation of the aperture voltage or the magnitude of the radiated power, which are defined by the antenna function. The radome function consists of an input geometric transformation, followed by the calculation of transmission and refraction effects, and finally an output geometric transformation. Because the transmission coefficient is dimensionless and refraction effects simply modify the internal path characteristics, the output is the modified aperture power magnitude or aperture voltage vector, which is dimensionally equivalent to the input in either case.

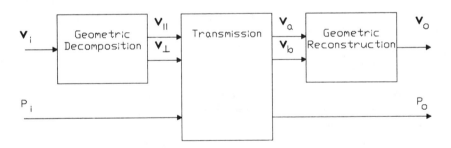

Figure 2.10 Radome Functional Diagram for the Transmitting Path

The input geometric transformations must separate the aperture voltage vector into components normal (perpendicular) and tangential (parallel) to the plane of incidence, at the point of intersection of the radome surface and the line-of-sight vector from the antenna to the point of interest.

Following this separation, we calculate a dimensionless transmission coefficient for both the normal (perpendicular) and tangential (parallel) component. We then multiply these transmission coefficients by the aperture voltage vector components to calculate the magnitudes of the two components of the voltage vector exiting the radome:

$$\mathbf{V}_a = \mathbf{V}_{\parallel} \tau_{\parallel} \tag{2.25}$$

$$\mathbf{V}_b = \mathbf{V}_{\perp} \tau_{\perp} \tag{2.26}$$

where

$\mathbf{V}_a$ = modified parallel component of the aperture voltage vector
$\mathbf{V}_{\parallel}$ = parallel component of the aperture voltage vector
$\tau_{\parallel}$ = parallel radome transmission component
$\mathbf{V}_b$ = modified perpendicular component of the aperture voltage vector
$\mathbf{V}_{\perp}$ = perpendicular component of the aperture voltage vector
$\tau_{\perp}$ = perpendicular radome transmission component

The refractive effect of the radome bends the propagation direction of the electric field intensity vector, as it is transmitted and reflected among the layers of the radome. Because the radome model assumes a locally planar situation, the directions of the two components of the aperture voltage vector exiting the radome are identical to those of the input aperture voltage vector.

The line-of-sight vector is usually considered to originate at the antenna, which is a reasonable approximation because the range to the point of interest is always significantly greater than the distance from the antenna to the radome.

Following the calculation of the transmission and refraction effects described above, we then need a final geometric transformation, which will convert the output aperture voltage vector components into a composite aperture voltage vector, $\mathbf{V}_0$, in the geometric reference system of the simulation.

For the case of a simpler simulation, which is not concerned with polarization effects, the input quantity to the radome function is typically the antenna radiated power. Because this power is a scalar quantity, we do no geometric transformations and simply multiply the radiated power by a transmission coefficient, which is generally some nominal value for the particular type of radome material:

$$P_0 = P_i \tau_p \tag{2.27}$$

where

P_0 = modified radiated power
P_i = radiated power
τ_p = radome power transmission coefficient

In the receiving path, the radome performs the same functions as in the transmitting path, except in reverse order. Figure 2.11 shows the functional diagram for this situation. Now the input quantity is the electric field intensity or power density entering the radome from some reflector or emitter.

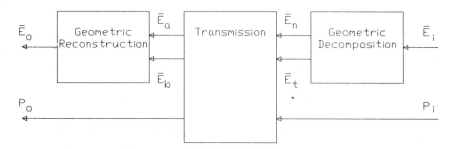

Figure 2.11 Radome Functional Diagram for the Receiving Path

For this case, the input geometric transformation separates the components of the incident electric field intensity, $\mathbf{E}_i$, into a parallel component, $\mathbf{E}_{\parallel}$, and a perpendicular component, $\mathbf{E}_{\perp}$, with respect to the plane of incidence. Each component is then multiplied by the appropriate transmission coefficient:

$$\mathbf{E}_a = \mathbf{E}_{\parallel} \tau_{\parallel} \tag{2.28}$$
$$\mathbf{E}_b = \mathbf{E}_{\perp} \tau_{\perp} \tag{2.29}$$

where
    $\mathbf{E}_a$ = modified parallel component of the electric field intensity
    $\mathbf{E}_{\parallel}$ = parallel component of the electric field intensity
    $\tau_{\parallel}$ = parallel radome transmission component
    $\mathbf{E}_b$ = modified perpendicular component of the electric field intensity
    $\mathbf{E}_{\perp}$ = perpendicular component of the electric field intensity
    $\tau_{\perp}$ = perpendicular radome transmission component

As in the case of the transmitting path, a refractive effect alters the directions of the electric field intensity component vectors within the radome layers.

The output geometric transformation then converts the two component electric field vectors $\mathbf{E}_A$ and $\mathbf{E}_B$ into the geometric reference system that is most convenient for the subsequent antenna function. The local geometric reference system of the antenna model is usually the most convenient.

Again, in a manner similar to the transmitting path situation, a simplistic simulation may be concerned only with scalar power density. In these situations, the output power density is calculated from the incident power density through the use of a nominal transmission coefficient:

$$P_0 = P_i \tau_p \qquad\qquad (2.30)$$

where

P_0 = modified incident power

P_i = incident power

τ_p = radome power transmission coefficient

This concludes the functional description of the processes involved in the radome model. Apparently, the elements common to both the transmitting and receiving paths are the transmission and refraction effects. The calculation of these effects, which are a function of the radome geometry, material composition, and the line-of-sight vector of the incident electromagnetic radiation, is the subject of Part III of this book.

2.3 SUMMARY

In this chapter, we presented the interactions among the components of a generic radar simulation. We showed how the antenna and radome models, which are developed in Parts II and III, may be applied to the problem of radar system simulation regardless of the specific type of radar we wish to simulate.

The applications for radar system models are quite diverse. Because the level of detail and accuracy will vary as a function of the particular simulation requirements, we addressed two extremes of simulation complexity. Most simulations will probably contain elements of one or the other extreme, making the discussions germane to the majority of practical applications.

PART II
ANTENNAS

This part introduces a series of mathematical models for the simulation of radar antennas. We derive and explain the models individually and combine them sequentially to produce a total antenna simulation. Because the models are each concerned with a particular effect and these effects are processed serially, their individual complexities are quite minimal, and we can explain them easily without discussing the corresponding simulation programs. Instead, the reader will find references to the appropriate model or algorithm in the program listings of Appendix A.

Chapter 3
Fundamental Principle

This chapter presents the basic concept behind a very useful and computationally simple mathematical model for a radar antenna. The technique can be easily structured for horns, illuminated reflectors, phased arrays, or whatever type of antenna is desired. This technique is readily applicable to both theoretical functions or measured data. Furthermore, computational simplicity of this model makes it exceptionally desirable for simulation, where simplicity means fast processing and small memory allocation.

The model presented here is actually so straightforward that its sheer simplicity may raise some skepticism as to its accuracy. So, to confirm its validity immediately, compare it to several classically derived antenna functions at the end of the chapter. The results speak for themselves.

3.1 DERIVATION OF THE GAIN ALGORITHM

To begin, consider a generic antenna gain pattern—any antenna pattern. First of all, it must have a main (or primary) lobe more or less centered on its central axis. Also, the pattern will have some secondary lobes, or sidelobes. These lobes will all have some gains and phase shifts associated with them. A generic pattern will generally appear as shown in Figure 3.1.

This figure shows the normalized dB power gain, A'_p, as a function of the angle between the antenna's central axis or boresight and the line-of-sight vector to the radar target or source. This angle is often referred to as the look angle, and may be composed of azimuth and elevation components. The decibel (dB) is the well known logarithmic expression of power gain according to the following relationship:

$$A_p = 10 \log(G_p) = 10 \log (G_v^2) = 20 \log (G_v)$$

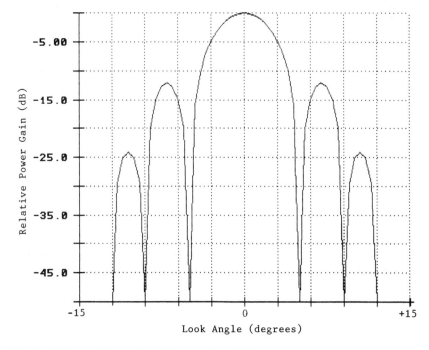

Fig. 3.1 Typical Normalized Power Gain Pattern

where

A_p = power gain, in dB

G_p = multiplicative power gain

G_v = multiplicative voltage gain

The shape, amplitude, and angular lobe widths of a particular antenna gain pattern are, of course, functions of its specific type, aperture, geometry, and illumination function. However, an algorithm that allows adequate control of these parameters' effects can duplicate any antenna gain pattern. If this algorithm is easier to use than the exact mathematical function for the particular antenna, we will save processing time and memory space. Furthermore, if one basic function applies to any antenna, we will not have to switch antenna types in a simulation. The following derivation of an antenna voltage gain function satisfies all these requirements.

Let us start the mathematical derivation. A simple sinusoid will produce a generally acceptable shape. If θ is the angular distance from the central axis of the antenna, we may write an expression for a simple sinusoidal function of θ:

$$F = \sin\theta \tag{3.1}$$

The use of a shaping exponent, C, will peak or flatten the shape of the function. This expression may be written as

$$F = (\sin\theta)^C \tag{3.2}$$

In the process of generating each lobe, the sinusoidal function must transit from a value of 0 through its maximum value of 1 and back to 0 as its argument increases from 0° to 180° or π radians. If it is necessary to generate several individual lobes, the range of the independent variable θ must be normalized for each lobe. If we define the upper and lower angular boundaries of a lobe as θ_u and θ_l, respectively, the function becomes

$$F = \left\{ \sin\left[\left(\frac{\theta - \theta_l}{\theta_u - \theta_l} \right) \pi \right] \right\}^C \tag{3.3}$$

For this derivation, the normalized voltage gain, A_v', is expressed in a quantity called *decibel voltage gain* (dBvg) with respect to the peak amplitude of the main lobe. This concept is introduced with the following definition:

$$A_v' = 10 \log(G_v')$$

where
$\quad A_v' =$ decibel voltage gain in dBvg
$\quad G_v' =$ multiplicative voltage gain

Although this definition is somewhat unconventional, it permits us to change from logarithmic gain to decimal gain in both power and voltage quantities with the same mathematical process:

Logarithmic gain $= 10 \log(\text{decimal gain})$

Thus, we no longer need to change coefficients back and forth between 10 and 20 depending on whether we are processing power or voltage gain. Actually, this definition is no less conventional than the generally accepted practice of expressing 10 log(area/1.0 square meter) as dBsm (dB square meters), a common means for quantifying the radar cross section of aircraft as a "dB-like" quantity. The only thing to remember is that dBvg is voltage gain expressed as a logarithmic (dB-like) quantity and *not* absolute dB, a power ratio, which may be expressed as a function of voltage gain.

In the process of developing this function, some experimentation revealed that a lower limit of -100 dBvg and a variable upper limit of M (in $-$dBvg from 0 dBvg) permitted us to apply the gain function to a wide variety of antenna gain lobes. Establishing these two limits sets the amplitude range R of the function as

$$R = M - (-100) = M + 100 \qquad (3.4)$$

Then, multiplying this range by the function of (3.3), and adding the lower limit, mathematically normalizes the function to the desired range and provides the resulting expression for A'_v, the normalized voltage gain:

$$F = A'_v$$
$$A'_v = \left\{ \sin\left[\left(\frac{\theta - \theta_l}{\theta_u - \theta_l} \right) \pi \right] \right\}^C (M + 100) - 100 \qquad (3.5)$$

Typically, the nature of an antenna gain pattern is such that sequential lobes produce phase shifts that alternate between 0 and π (0° and 180°). The algorithm accommodates this alternation through the assignment of a lobe number, an integer N, such that $N = 1$ for the lobe closest to the central axis of the pattern ($\theta = 0$) and increases with each subsequent lobe, as shown in Figure 3.2.

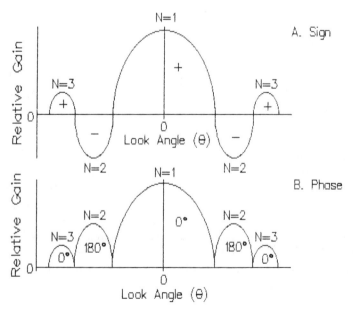

Fig. 3.2 Lobe Numbering, Phase, and Sign Relationships

Therefore, we may establish phase shift ϕ simply as a function of whether the lobe number N is odd or even as follows:

$\phi = 0$ (0°) for odd N
$\phi = \pi$ (180°) for even N

Summarizing the algorithm development to this point, we can specify the coefficients for each lobe:

N = the lobe number, an integer
M = the maximum amplitude in dBvg
θ_l = the lower angular boundary
θ_u = the upper angular boundary
C = the exponential shaping coefficient

The mathematical functions are (from (3.5))

$$F = \left\{ \sin\left[\left(\frac{\theta - \theta_l}{\theta_u - \theta_l} \right) \pi \right] \right\}^C (M + 100) - 100$$

and

$$\phi = \pi \mid \cos(N\pi/2)\mid \qquad (3.6)$$

Actually, we may implement the phase shift relationship as the function of (3.6) or simply as an IF/THEN rule following the previously described logic for odd and even lobe numbers. Although a few cases do not adhere to this convention for phase shift, this convention is valid for the majority of antenna patterns. In the instances for which it is not valid, we must explicitly assign the phase shift of each lobe.

As it now stands, the voltage gain function A'_v represents an expression for normalized dB voltage gain. As such, its maximum value is 0, representing a decimal or multiplicative voltage gain, G'_v, as follows:

$$G'_v = 10^{A'_v/10} = 10^0 = 1.0 \qquad (3.7)$$

where

G'_v = multiplicative voltage gain
A'_v = dB voltage gain in dBvg

We will extend this function to an actual voltage gain rather than a relative ("normalized") voltage gain later in this chapter. For now, it is prudent to

explore the function's versatility and to verify the function against some classically derived antenna functions. We can perform both operations more conveniently in terms of normalized gain.

The antenna gain pattern of Figure 3.1 is now repeated as Figure 3.3 along
with the coefficients used to generate the lobes. Note that this is a normalized
power gain (A_p') pattern, rather than a normalized voltage gain (A_v') pattern. It
was constructed simply by multiplying the voltage gain pattern produced by (3.5)
by a factor of 2 because

$$G_p' = G_v'^2 = \left(10^{A_v'/10}\right)^2 = 10^{A_p'/10} \tag{3.8}$$
$$2A_v' = A_p'$$

The value of C (0.045) was chosen in this case because it was experi-
mentally determined to cause the function to produce a purely sinusoidal function
in the decimal voltage gain domain. In other words, this sample function ap-
proximates a 180° sinusoidal curve normalized to the angular boundaries and
amplitude of each lobe.

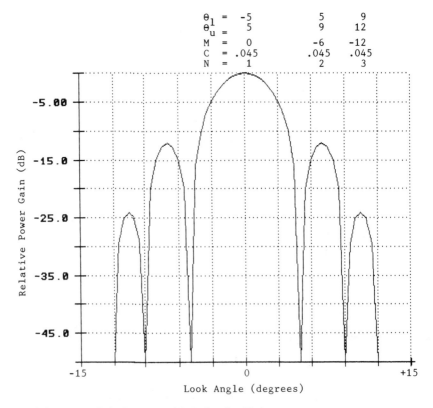

Fig. 3.3 Power Gain Pattern with Lobe Coefficients

We do not present this simple example to emulate any particular antenna gain function, but rather to illustrate how we can control the shape of the individual lobes by adjusting the value of the exponent C. Figure 3.4 shows the power gain pattern generated with the value of C increased from 0.045 to 0.10. This change results in a narrowing or peaking of the lobe shape.

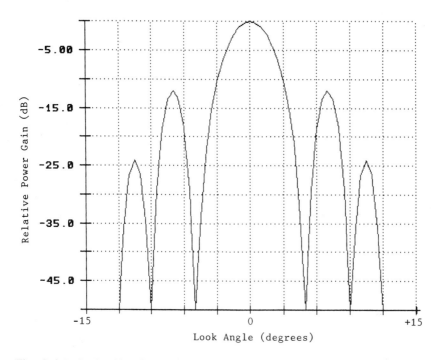

Fig. 3.4 Lobe Peaking by Increasing C to 0.1

Conversely, reducing the value of C to 0.02 results in the power gain pattern shown in Figure 3.5, which exhibits a widening or flattening of the lobe shape. These examples demonstrate how we may tailor each lobe of a gain pattern to fit a desired shape simply by adjusting a single coefficient.

In these cases, because the amplitude of the gain is expressed in a logarithmic quantity dB, it is really a representation of the absolute value of the gains for each lobe with no regard for the effect of phase shift differences among the individual lobes. When we plot the actual (decimal) values for the lobe gains as in the next example case, we may represent the phase shift relationships by assigning a negative value to the lobes with a 180° phase shift.

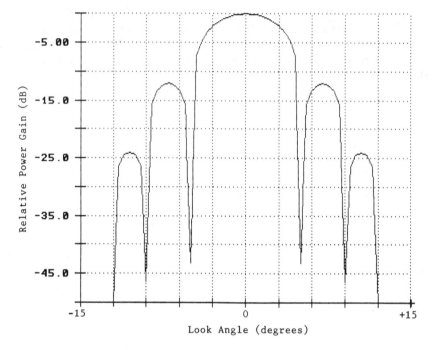

Fig. 3.5 Lobe Flattening by Decreasing C to 0.02

3.2 VERIFICATION OF THE ALGORITHM

At this point, we have established the basic algorithm for an antenna gain pattern and have demonstrated its shaping versatility. The algorithm has been used to simulate a fairly simple sinusoidal function. Obviously, for this sample case, the complexity of the algorithm actually exceeds that of the function which it is modeling. But gain functions derived from illumination functions for actual antenna apertures are significantly more complex than this sample case. The merit of the algorithm lies in its ability to model *any* antenna gain function. Thus, a verification process should confirm this ability for a variety of gain functions ranging from the simple to the very complex.

For the first verification case, we fit the algorithm to the simplest theoretical example of an antenna—a current strip with a uniform, temporally sinusoidal current distribution of a specific length. This situation is illustrated in Figure 3.6, which shows a uniform current distribution of length L in the z direction.

The normalized voltage gain, which is the far-field electric field magnitude, can be expressed as the integral of the sinusoidally varying function over the length of the current distribution as follows:

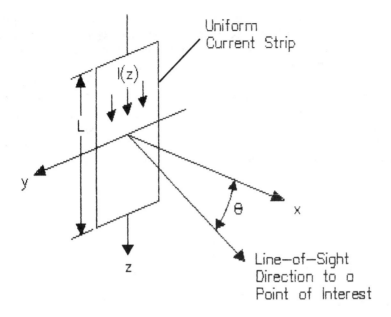

Fig. 3.6 Current Strip in the Rectangular Coordinate System

$$f(u) = \int_L I(z)e^{jkuz}dz$$

where

u = sinθ

θ = look angle

L = length of the current strip along the z-axis

k = wavenumber ($2\pi/\lambda$)

λ = wavelength

$I(z)$ = current

Evaluation of this integral, which is the far-field solution, results in the familiar "sin(x)/x" or sinc function:

$$f(u) = \frac{\sin(\pi uL/\lambda)}{(\pi uL/\lambda)} \tag{3.9}$$

The sinc function is often used as a general simulation for a variety of antennas. We can vary the lobe widths simply by changing the L/λ ratio. However, this adjustment to the sinc function changes all lobe widths simultaneously and proportionally. The algorithm of (3.5) offers a great deal more versatility than the simple sinc function by permitting us to control independently the shape and angular width of each lobe. The purpose here is to fit the algorithm to the sinc function as the most basic verification case.

As an example case, the use of an L/λ ratio of 13/1 in the sinc function results in the voltage gain pattern of Figure 3.7. The algorithm is fitted to the first three lobes of the sinc function of Figure 3.7 by first defining the angular boundaries of each lobe, then assigning the appropriate maximum gain values to the lobes, and finally shaping each lobe by adjusting the shaping exponent. This sequential procedure is the recommended approach and eliminates unnecessary reiterations.

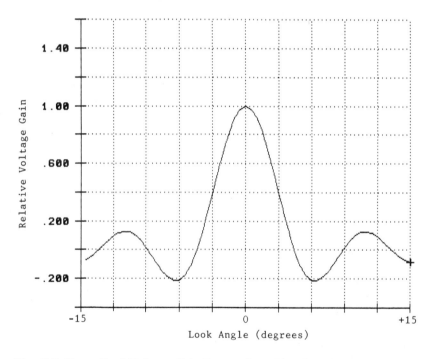

Fig. 3.7 Normalized Voltage Gain Pattern from Sinc Function

Table 3.1 gives the angular lobe boundaries from the pattern of Figure 3.7:

Table 3.1

Lobe (N)	Lower Boundary $\theta_l(N)$	Upper Boundary $\theta_u(N)$
1	−4.4	4.4
2	4.4	8.9
3	8.9	13.3

Because the pattern of Figure 3.7 is a normalized voltage gain pattern, we can read the maximum actual gain values for each lobe from the pattern, then calculate the dB voltage gain values for insertion into the gain algorithm as follows:

$$M = 10 \log(G_v) \tag{3.10}$$

where

M = maximum dB voltage gain of the lobe in dBvg
G_v = maximum decimal voltage gain of the lobe

This equation results in the following maximum gain values for the lobes as shown in Table 3.2.

Table 3.2

Lobe Number (N)	Maximum Decimal Voltage Gain $G_v(N)$	Maximum dB Voltage Gain $M(N)$
1	1.0	0.0
2	0.21	−6.8
3	0.13	−8.9

We can determine the values for the shaping exponents for each lobe through an iterative process of adjustment and comparison with the desired shape. An initial value of 0.045, the value discussed previously for obtaining a sinusoidal shape, is a good starting point. With a little experimentation, we determine the values for the shaping exponents (Table 3.3).

Table 3.3

Lobe (N)	Shaping Exponent C(N)
1	0.055
2	0.045
3	0.040

Finally, the phase shift associated with each lobe is assigned according to the previously described rule: 0° for odd N, 180° for even N.

Using the coefficients determined in Table 3.3, we can produce a voltage gain pattern that fits the theoretical sinc function of Figure 3.7. The resulting pattern is illustrated in Figure 3.8, which shows the original sinc function again for ease of comparison. Note that we handle the phase shift simply by multiplying the gain of the even-numbered lobe ($N = 2$) by -1, which is mathematically equivalent to a 180° phase shift. This case illustrates the ease with which the algorithm may be fitted to a gain pattern and the quality of the fit obtained.

Voltage gain functions of actual antennas are often considerably more complex than the simple sinc function. Voltage gain can be mathematically stated as the integral of the aperture illumination function over the area of the aperture. Thus, a voltage gain function for a rectangular aperture is most easily described in terms of the height and width of the aperture, with the illumination as a function of rectangular dimensions y and z. In the case of a circular aperture, the voltage gain can be readily described in terms of the diameter of the aperture with the illumination as a function of radius r.

Figure 3.9 illustrates a rectangular aperture on the y-z plane of a reference system. For this case, it is interesting to present some equations to illustrate the mathematical complexity of some actual voltage gain functions for both rectangular and circular apertures. The expression for the voltage gain of a rectangular aperture is

$$F(u,v) = \int_{-W/2}^{W/2}\int_{-H/2}^{H/2} g(y,z)e^{-j2\pi(yu+zv)}dydz \tag{3.11}$$

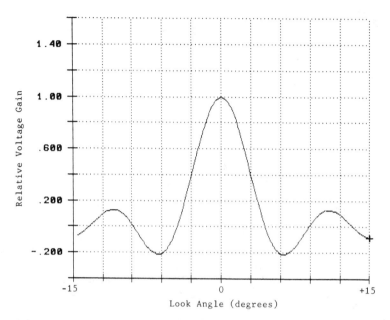

Fig. 3.8(a) Sinc Function-Generated Gain Pattern

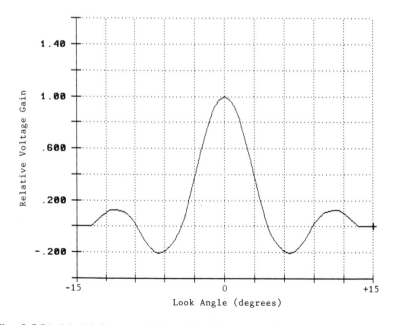

Fig. 3.8(b) Model-Generated Fit to Sinc Pattern

where

W	=	aperture width in the y direction
H	=	aperture height in the z direction
u	=	$(1/\lambda)\sin\theta\cos\phi$
v	=	$(1/\lambda)\sin\theta\sin\phi$
λ	=	wavelength in the same units as W and H
$g(y,z)$	=	illumination function

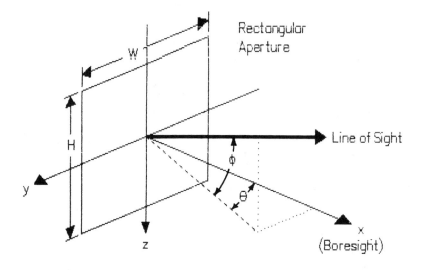

Fig. 3.9 Rectangular Aperture in a $y - z$ Plane

Similarly, the expression for the voltage gain of a circular aperture of diameter D is

$$F(U) = 2\pi \int_0^{D/2} g(r)J_0(2\pi rU)r\,dr \qquad (3.12)$$

where

U	=	$\sin\theta/\lambda$
r	=	$(y^2 + z^2)^{1/2}$
J_0	=	zero-order Bessel function
$g(r)$	=	illumination function

Obviously, we would need considerable processing time to implement mathematics such as these in a simulation. The illumination functions may be fairly involved mathematical quantities, and the integral or multiple integral may not have an explicit solution in many cases, forcing the simulation into a numerical integration.

However, if the gain algorithm can successfully model such complex gain functions as easily and accurately as the simple sinc function, we can avoid such mathematical complexity and establish its utility in simulating antenna gain patterns. This capability is demonstrated by fitting the algorithm to several actual voltage gain patterns simply by changing the lobe coefficients. We determine the coefficients for each lobe through the same sequential process used to fit the algorithm to the sinc function in the previous example. Figures 3.10, 3.11, and 3.12 illustrate the fit obtained for these cases. The illumination functions range from simple geometric relationships to complex power series, which represent a variety of possible cases.

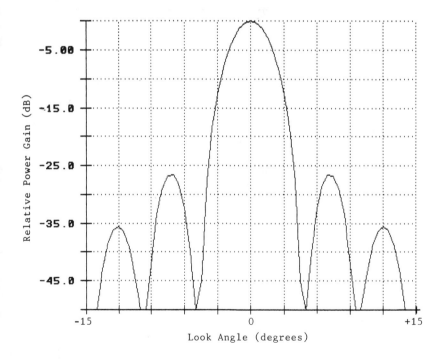

Fig. 3.10(a) Example of Gain Pattern from Triangular Illumination

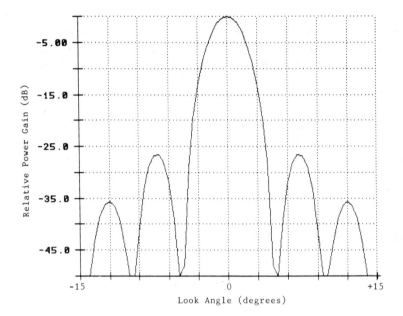

Fig. 3.10(b) Model-Generated Fit to Triangular Pattern

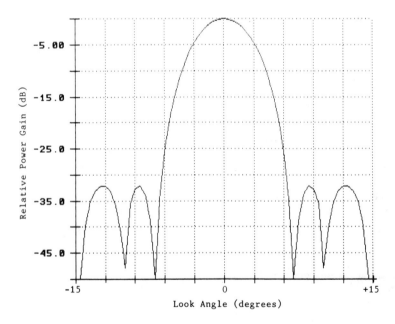

Fig. 3.11(a) Example of Gain Pattern from Taylor Illumination

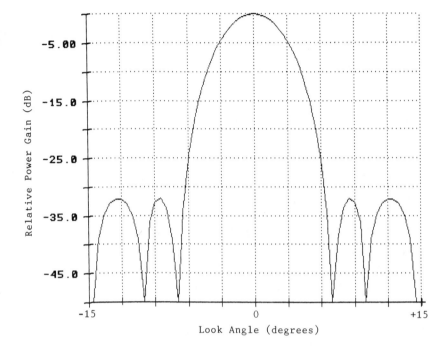

Fig. 3.11(b) Model-Generated Fit to Taylor Pattern

Consider the implications of the results shown in these figures on a simulation. The figures show changes among several different and complex antenna gain patterns, changes effected simply by using a different set of five constants for each lobe. Therefore, the process of changing antenna gain functions does not require the following:

• restructuring of subroutine calls;
• additional mathematical or trigonometric functions;
• additional variables or coefficients.

Only a simple fitting process is required, which can be implemented as a pre-processing element to determine the necessary coefficients for the algorithm.

In a typical implementation, we can determine the lobe coefficients either by generating the actual voltage gain pattern off line from an actual mathematical function, or by obtaining the pattern from measured data and fitting the gain algorithm to this pattern. Thus, the gain algorithm, rather than the actual voltage gain function, would be programmed into the simulation, resulting in significant savings in processing time.

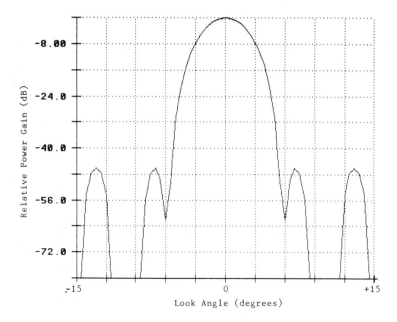

Fig. 3.12(a) Example of Gain Pattern from Hamming Illumination

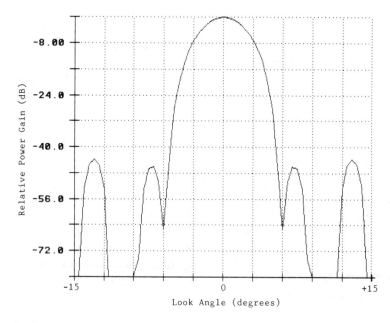

Fig. 3.12(b) Model-Generated Fit to Hamming Pattern

Notice that the functions to which the model was fitted are quite different and complex, and that in all cases the fit is quite excellent. Also consider the impact that the complexity of the actual functions would have on their implementation in software. As previously discussed, multiple numerical integrations such as these would consume a great deal of processing time—time which is saved by the simplicity of the gain algorithm. Even the use of measured or mathematically generated data as a look-up table is less efficient than the gain algorithm, which is less complex than the interpolation mathematics required to support the look-up table. Also, the gain algorithm only requires the storage of the lobe coefficients, which occupies considerably less memory space than a matrix of gain values.

3.3 ACTUAL GAIN CALCULATIONS

Now that we have derived and verified the algorithm for a normalized antenna gain pattern, we must extend it to an actual gain. The peak gain, at the maximum point of the main lobe of an antenna gain pattern, can be considered a measure of how well the total radiated power is focused into a small, solid angle. If the total power were not focused, it would be radiated isotropically into a sphere. Thus, the expression for peak antenna power gain G_{pp} is

$$G_{pp} = \frac{\text{Solid Angle of a Sphere}}{\text{Solid Angle of Focus}}$$

A useful and popular approximation for the solid angle of focus is to consider all the power to be contained in the solid angle θ_h at which the power is half of its peak amplitude. In terms of normalized gain, this angle is at the -3 dB power gain point or the -1.5 dBvg voltage gain point of the gain pattern. Application of this concept results in the following equations for the peak power gain and peak voltage gain:

$$G_{pp} = 4\pi/(\theta_h)^2 \qquad (3.13)$$
$$G_{pv} = (G_{pp})^{1/2} = 2(\pi)^{1/2}/\theta_h \qquad (3.14)$$

where
G_{pp} = peak multiplicative power gain
G_{pv} = peak multiplicative voltage gain
θ_h = half-power full angle, in radians

In the case of an existing antenna, we can determine the peak voltage gain or peak power gain from the results of laboratory or field testing. If the peak power gain is the known quantity, we may obtain the peak voltage gain simply by finding the square root of the peak multiplicative power gain, as shown in (3.14). Often, the peak power gain is given in dB. In these cases, the value for the peak multiplicative voltage gain is calculated as

$$G_{pv} = 10^{(A_{pp}/20)} \qquad\qquad (3.15)$$

where A_{pp} is the peak dB power gain.

When the voltage gain algorithm is successfully fitted to a pattern, the half-power beamwidth may be calculated by setting the dB voltage gain expression of (3.5), equal to $M - 1.5$ and solving for θ. This results in:

$$\theta_h = 2 \left| \left[\frac{\sin^{-1}\left(\dfrac{100 + M - 1.5}{100 + M} \right)^{1/C}}{\pi} \right] (\theta_u - \theta_l) + \theta_l \right| \qquad (3.16)$$

where

C = shaping coefficient of the main lobe
θ_u = upper angular boundary of the main lobe
θ_l = lower angular boundary of the main lobe
M = maximum dBvg of the lobe (0 for normalized main lobe)

The peak dB voltage gain is found simply by inserting the result into (3.14).

Regardless of the means by which we obtain the actual peak voltage gain, it is introduced into the algorithm simply by adding its dBvg value to the expression for normalized dB voltage gain, or by multiplying its decimal value by the expression for normalized decimal voltage gain:

$$A_v = F + 10 \log(G_{pv}) \qquad\qquad (3.17)$$
$$G_v = 10^{F/10} G_{pv} \qquad\qquad (3.18)$$

where
A_v = actual (not normalized) dB voltage gain, in dBvg
G_{pv} = peak multiplicative voltage gain
F = normalized dB voltage gain function from (3.5)

3.4 LOOK-ANGLE CONVENTION

Before concluding this chapter, we should briefly discuss the angle θ, which is the driving independent variable for the algorithm. In a simulation, θ would simply be the look angle to the target with respect to the antenna's central axis as shown in Figure 3.13. As this figure shows, if the look angle is described in spherical coordinates, then θ is simply the axial angle.

However, if the look angle is described in rectangular coordinates, we need either a conversion to spherical coordinates or the geometric calculation of θ from the rectangular components θ_a and θ_e. This conversion, shown in Figure 3.14, is accomplished with either of the following expressions:

$$\theta = \cos^{-1}(\cos\theta_a \cos\theta_e) \tag{3.19}$$
$$\theta = \sin^{-1}\{[(\sin\theta_e)^2 + (\cos\theta_e \sin\theta_a)^2]^{1/2}\} \tag{3.20}$$

where
θ = composite look angle
θ_a = azimuth look angle component
θ_e = elevation look angle component

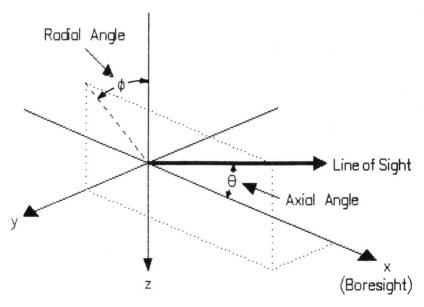

Fig. 3.13 Look Angle in a Spherical Coordinate System

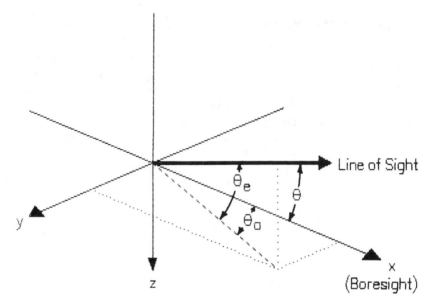

Fig. 3.14 Look Angle in a Rectangular Coordinate System

3.5 SUMMARY

This chapter described the derivation and verification of a fundamental algorithm for simulation of an antenna's gain pattern as a function of look angle. The gain algorithm offers the advantages of computational simplicity as well as ease of change among different patterns with no structural change to the basic function. Another distinct advantage is that when we require the simulation of an actual antenna, we may easily fit the algorithm to measured data rather than to a theoretical function.

At this point, the algorithm is in a basic form. It represents the ideal case of a continuous, circular aperture because it produces a pattern that is both radially constant and axially symmetrical, as illustrated in the three-dimensional pattern of Figure 3.15.

In other words, the gain is purely a function of the look angle θ with no regard to the effect of ϕ, the rotational or radial angle. In the following chapters of Part II, we apply the gain algorithm to several types of actual antennas, and make additions to handle the radial modulations produced by different aperture shapes as well as the axial distortions introduced through such factors as irregular horn shape and the electronic pointing of planar arrays.

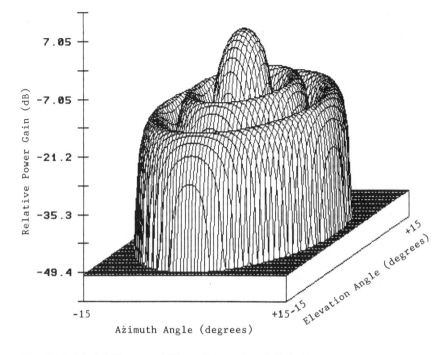

Fig. 3.15 Model-Generated Three-Dimensional Gain Pattern

Throughout this chapter, we used the term "gain pattern" to describe the gain of an antenna as a function of the look angle. However, because the only pattern an antenna can have is gain as a function of look angle, most practicing antenna engineers prefer to drop the "gain" and refer to this simply as the "pattern." Because this chapter established the basic mathematical gain function and described its capability to produce patterns, the seeming redundancy in the term "gain pattern" was used so that readers unfamiliar with antenna design conventions and terminology could understand the mathematics. In subsequent chapters, however, we will use the term "pattern" to describe gain as a function of look angle to be consistent with the preferred convention.

Chapter 4

General Application

This chapter begins the process of developing a usable antenna pattern simulation by integrating the algorithms formulated in Chapter 3 into a basic model. Additionally, we develop some mathematics that extends the capabilities of the antenna pattern algorithm. Although this algorithm achieved a reasonable fit in the previously described verification cases, it requires some additional improvements to simulate properly the gain patterns of actual antennas.

First, the algorithms developed earlier are structured into a very basic antenna pattern model. This model is the foundation on which the final simulation will be built. We develop the simulation by progressively adding functions to the basic model in the remaining chapters of Part II.

Next, the lobe shaping capability is enhanced. The use of a shaping coefficient to peak and flatten the lobes has some limitations, but we can readily overcome them by adding a simple geometric function.

We then add the capability to produce a nonsymmetrical pattern. Many antennas have a gain pattern with lobes that are wider in the azimuth plane than in the elevation plane and *vice versa*.

Finally, we develop the capability to modulate the amplitude of the gain pattern sidelobes as a function of the rotational or radial angle. Actual antennas do not necessarily exhibit the radially constant characteristic produced by the basic gain function.

In this chapter, we derive the means for producing these additional effects and integrate them into the basic antenna pattern model. In all cases, we keep the mathematics as simple as possible, in the spirit of minimizing the computational complexity and the subsequent processing time in a simulation.

4.1 STRUCTURING A BASIC PATTERN MODEL

In Chapter 3, we derived the following algorithm, or function, for simulating the normalized voltage pattern of a lobe of an antenna:

$$F = \left\{ \sin \left[\left(\frac{\theta - \theta_l}{\theta_u - \theta_l} \right) \pi \right] \right\}^C (M + 100) - 100 \qquad (4.1)$$

where

F = voltage pattern as a function of θ in dBvg
θ = look angle, or axial angle
θ_l = lower angular boundary of the lobe
θ_u = upper angular boundary of the lobe
M = maximum amplitude in dBvg
C = shaping coefficient

The coefficients θ_l, θ_u, M, and C are set-up or system characteristics associated with a particular lobe. The forcing function or independent variable is the look angle. Notice that the angular coefficients may be defined in terms of either degrees or radians as long as the convention chosen is consistent within the equation.

Chapter 3 also discussed how the phase shift associated with a particular lobe may be either specified or defined as a function of that lobe's position with respect to the boresight. The first lobe has a phase shift of 0° (0 radians), the second lobe has a phase shift of 180° (π radians), and so on, alternating through the total number of lobes. Thus, if the lobes are numbered consecutively starting with the lobe nearest the boresight, the phase shift may be obtained from the following rule:

$$\begin{aligned} S_p &= 0 \quad \text{for odd } N \\ S_p &= \pi \quad \text{for even } N \end{aligned} \qquad (4.2)$$

where

S_p = phase shift in radians
N = lobe number

In some cases, we are interested not in the phase of an RF signal but only in the absolute amplitude. However, in these cases, the amplitude of the voltage gain must carry a sign that depicts the relative phase relationship among the lobes in the presence of an RF signal of some phase, regardless of that particular phase. Because a 180° phase shift is mathematically equal to a negative amplitude with a 0° phase shift, we may use the following rule to obtain a lobe sign coefficient:

$$\begin{aligned} SL &= 1 \quad \text{for odd } N \\ SL &= -1 \quad \text{for even } N \end{aligned} \qquad (4.3)$$

where

SL = lobe sign coefficient
N = lobe number

We can now express the normalized lobe gain, in its various forms, in terms of the voltage gain from (4.1) and the lobe sign coefficient from (4.3):

$$A'_v = F \tag{4.4}$$

$$A'_p = 2F \tag{4.5}$$

$$G'_v = [10^{(F/10)}]SL \tag{4.6}$$

$$G'_p = [10^{(2F/10)}]SL = G_v'^2 \tag{4.7}$$

where

A'_v = normalized voltage gain in dBvg
A'_p = normalized power gain in dB
G'_v = normalized multiplicative voltage gain
G'_p = normalized multiplicative power gain

Chapter 3 also discussed several means for obtaining the peak power gain G_{pp} and peak voltage gain G_{pv} as a function of half-power beamwidth. Regardless of the means by which we obtain these quantities, they may be used to convert the normalized gains to actual gains as follows:

$$A_v = F + A_{pv} \tag{4.8}$$

$$A_p = 2F + A_{pp} = 2(F + A_{pv}) = 2A_v \tag{4.9}$$

$$G_v = [10^{A_v/10}]SL \tag{4.10}$$

$$G_p = [10^{A_p/10}]SL = G_v^2 \tag{4.11}$$

where

A_v = voltage gain in dBvg
A_p = power gain in dB
G_v = multiplicative voltage gain
G_p = multiplicative power gain
A_{pv} = peak voltage gain in dBvg
$A_{pp} = 2A_{pv}$ = peak power gain in dB

Notice that the logarithmic quantities, dB voltage gain and dB power gain, cannot use the lobe sign coefficient as a multiplier. This inability can be a source of error in a simulation. Therefore, in converting back and forth between multiplicative and dB quantities, we must be careful to use the absolute value of the multiplicative quantity when converting to a dB quantity.

As discussed in Chapter 3, the look angle may be determined from the azimuth and elevation components according to the following expression:

$$\theta = \sin^{-1} \left\{ \left[(\sin\theta_e)^2 + (\cos\theta_e \sin\theta_a) \right]^2 \right\}^{1/2} \tag{4.12}$$

where

θ = composite look angle

θ_a = azimuth component of θ

θ_e = elevation component of θ

Finally, the algorithms and functions summarized above may be combined into a simple antenna voltage pattern model as illustrated in Figure 4.1. The

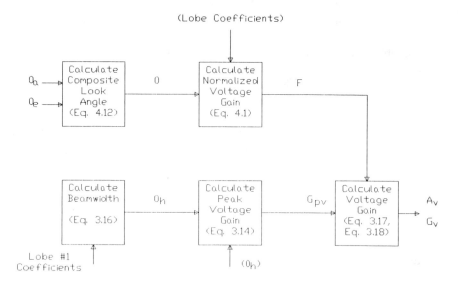

Fig. 4.1 Basic Voltage Pattern Model Structure

voltage pattern model is considered to be the fundamental element throughout this section, and the reader should be able to convert to power gain as required, using the relationships of (4.9) and (4.11).

Functionally speaking, the composite look angle is first determined from its azimuth and elevation components. This look angle is compared to the upper and lower angular limits defined for each lobe in the system, to determine the lobe number and other appropriate lobe coefficients to be used. Then, the normalized voltage pattern is calculated using the selected coefficients.

Because the calculations of beamwidth and peak voltage gain are not functions of the look angle, they may be performed only once in an off-line process for a particular set of lobe coefficients. Therefore, these computations do not affect processing time. Notice that the half-power beamwidth and peak voltage gain may be calculated from the model coefficients or simply inserted at the user's discretion, permitting the use of manufacturer's data or test data when they are available. Finally, we obtain the actual (absolute, not normalized) voltage gain as a function of the normalized voltage pattern and the peak voltage gain. The mathematical sign of the multiplicative voltage gain may be obtained from the alternating lobe convention or inserted by the user.

Notice that a normalized voltage pattern may be obtained simply by setting the value of A_{pv} equal to 0.0. In terms of the characteristics of a gain pattern, it is more convenient to work in terms of the normalized gain. Calculation of the actual gain has no effect on the relative characteristics of the pattern, only on the actual magnitude of the gain.

For example, the normalized voltage gain pattern illustrated in Figure 4.2 is obtained by using an elevation look angle component of 0.0 and varying the azimuth look angle component from $-15°$ to $15°$. Note that in this case, because θ_e is set to 0:

$$\theta = \theta_a$$

and as θ varies through its range, we obtain the appropriate shape, amplitude, and sign for each lobe.

Figure 4.3 shows a three-dimensional plot of the same normalized voltage pattern function. In this case, both the azimuth and elevation components of the look angle are varied through the range of $-15°$ to $15°$. It is quite obvious at this point that the simulation produces a very idealized, symmetrical pattern.

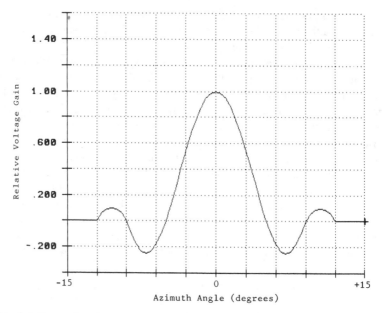

Fig. 4.2 Example of a Model-Generated Voltage Pattern

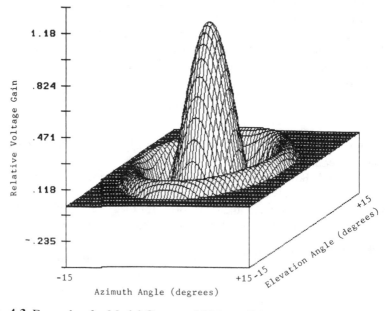

Fig. 4.3 Example of a Model-Generated Voltage Pattern

4.2 LOBE SHAPING

We demonstrated in Chapter 3 that the voltage gain function produces a lobe shape, which can be widened or made more rounded at the peak by decreasing the value of the shaping coefficient C. Conversely, the lobe may be narrowed or made more pointed at the peak by increasing the value of C.

However, if the value of C is increased significantly above the value of 0.046, then along with the desired narrowing of the peak some very undesirable distortion occurs at the zero-crossing point between lobes. We will illustrate this distortion with an example.

Assume that the dB power gain pattern illustrated in Figure 4.4 is the desired pattern. This pattern consists of a main lobe and two sidelobes.

We may obtain a reasonably good fit to this pattern, shown in Figure 4.5, by using the basic function with the listed coefficients. This pattern excellently fits the desired pattern through the outer region of the main lobe and the sidelobes. However, in the region of the main lobe near 0°, the simulated pattern is somewhat wider than desired.

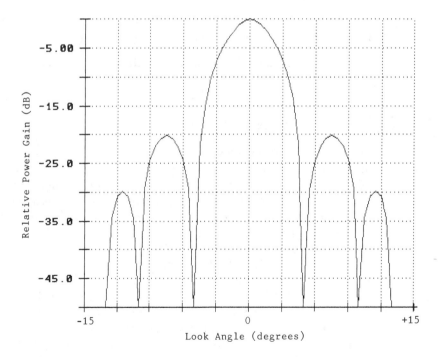

Fig. 4.4 Power Pattern to Be Simulated

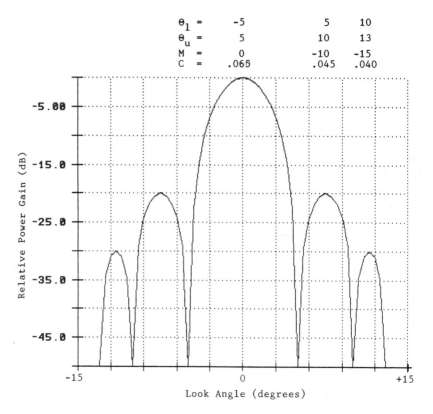

θ_l =	-5	5	10
θ_u =	5	10	13
M =	0	-10	-15
C =	.065	.045	.040

Fig. 4.5 Initial Fit to the Desired Power Pattern

This deviation of the fitted pattern from the desired pattern may seem trivial. However, its true significance is a function of the intended use for the model. For example, if the modeled pattern is part of a monopulse tracking radar simulation, the shape of the gain pattern near the boresight axis has direct bearing on the slope and linearity of the tracking error function. This situation is thoroughly addressed in Chapter 7, but it is sufficient to say here that we really need a means for achieving a better fit in this region of the gain pattern.

We may obtain a better fit to the desired pattern near the boresight axis by increasing C, the shaping coefficient, to a value of 0.10. This results in the pattern of Figure 4.6. Although it is a very good fit to the desired one in the near-boresight region, this pattern also introduces some serious distortion in the modeled pattern at the zeros or zero crossings of the pattern's main lobe.

This distortion is more clearly shown in the voltage gain pattern for the same lobe coefficients, which is illustrated in Figure 4.7. Actual antennas simply do not make abrupt changes such as this in the slope of the gain function at the zero crossing.

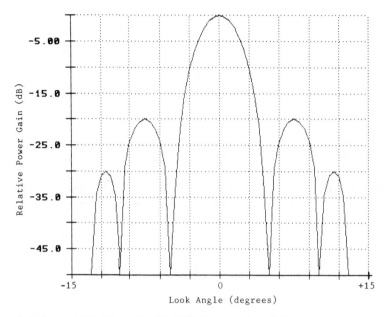

Fig. 4.6 Second Fit Attempt with $C(1)$ Increased to 0.1

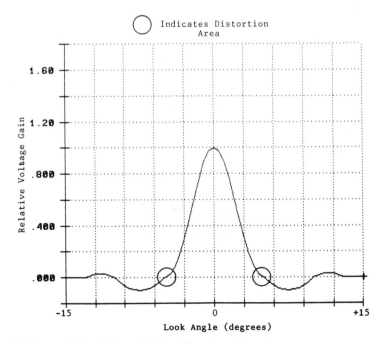

Fig. 4.7 Second-Fit Voltage Pattern Showing Distortion

Therefore, we require a means for adjusting the near-boresight lobe shape without distorting the function at the zero crossings. This is adjustment accomplished through a simple geometric process called *triangular shaping*. The process is so named because it is simply a means by which a triangular-shaped function such as the one illustrated in Figure 4.8, which peaks at the center of the lobe, is added to the voltage gain function.

The triangular function may be weighted or given a maximum amplitude in some desired proportion to the voltage gain function. After the addition of the two functions, the amplitude of the combined function is renormalized to the maximum value of the original voltage gain function. The effect of this process is that of making the combined function shape more peaked, or narrow at the center of the lobe, where the triangular function is at maximum. The effect is minimal at the angular boundaries of the lobe because the triangular function approaches zero at these boundaries.

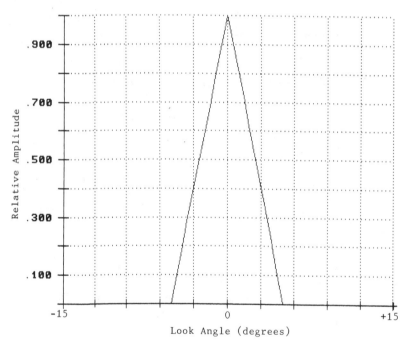

Fig. 4.8 Triangular Shaping Function

We easily implement this function as a variation of the classic equation of a straight line:

$$y = Mx + B$$

where

y = ordinate value
x = abscissa value
M = slope
B = y-axis intercept

In this application, the abscissa is the look angle and the ordinate is multiplicative voltage gain. Also, the slope is given a different symbol in order to avoid confusion with M, the maximum dB voltage gain for a lobe. These modifications result in the following expression:

$$T = S\theta_n + B \qquad (4.13)$$

where

T = triangular function value
θ_n = look angle, in radians, normalized to the lobe center
S = slope
B = voltage gain at the lobe center

The center of the lobe may be expressed in terms of the angular lobe boundaries as follows:

$$\theta_c = \theta_l + (\theta_u - \theta_l)/2 \qquad (4.14)$$

where

θ_c = lobe center angle
θ_l = lower angular lobe boundary
θ_u = upper angular lobe boundary

Next, we may write the expression for the look angle normalized to the lobe center in terms of the actual look angle. Because the triangular function is intended to be symmetrical on either side of the lobe center, the normalized look angle is conveniently expressed as an absolute value:

$$\theta_n = |\theta_c - \theta|$$ (4.15)

where θ is the composite look angle.

The maximum value of the triangular function is that of the y-intercept of the line equation. Because this function must be related to the maximum value of the normalized voltage pattern function at lobe center by some weighting coefficient, the maximum value is easily expressed as the following product:

$$B = W(10^{M/10})$$ (4.16)

where
   B = maximum value of the triangular function
   W = triangular weighting coefficient
   M = maximum normalized voltage gain of the lobe in dBvg

The slope is then easily calculated as the maximum value of the triangular function divided by half the angular lobe width:

$$S = B/((\theta_u - \theta_l)/2)$$ (4.17)

Substituting (4.14) through (4.17) into (4.13) gives the final expression for the triangular function:

$$T = W(10^{M/10}) \left[\frac{-|\theta_c - \theta|}{(\theta_u - \theta_l)/2} + 1 \right]$$ (4.18)

Finally, the triangular function is added to the voltage pattern and normalized to the maximum value of the voltage gain function as follows:

$$F_T = 10 \log \left[(T + 10^{F/10})/(W + 1) \right]$$ (4.19)

where F = normalized voltage gain from (4.1)

We insert the triangular shaping function into the simulation by sequentially performing the calculations of (4.18) and (4.19) immediately following the normalized voltage gain function as illustrated in Figure 4.9. Note that the weighting coefficient W defines the weight of the triangular function with respect to the original voltage gain function. In other words, a weighting of 1.0 means the triangular function and the voltage gain function are weighted equally, a weighting of 0.5 means the triangular function has half the weighting of the voltage gain function, and so forth.

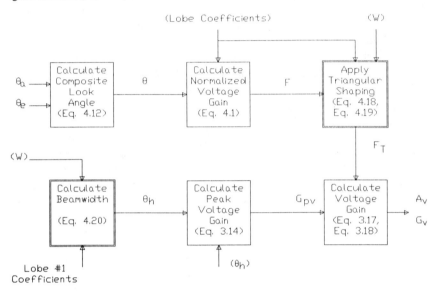

Fig. 4.9 Voltage Pattern Model with Triangular Shaping

Because the triangular shaping function affects the shape of the antenna gain pattern, it must also influence the peak voltage gain, when this quantity is calculated from the beamwidth determined from the voltage gain function. Therefore, we need to modify the expression for beamwidth, originally defined by (3.16). This modification results in the following expression:

$$F_t = 10 \log \left\{ \frac{W(10^{M/10}) \left[\dfrac{-|\theta|}{(\theta_u - \theta_l)/2} + 1 \right] + 10^{F/10}}{W + 1} \right\} \quad (4.20)$$

$$(F_t = M - 1.5 \text{ when } \theta = \theta_h/2)$$

where

θ_h = half-power beamwidth

F = normalized voltage gain function

We now include (4.20) in the functional flow of the model in place of (3.16), as Figure 4.9 illustrates. Because (4.20) does not permit an explicit solution, we actually determine the beamwidth by iteratively trying values of θ until a value of $(M - 1.5)$ is achieved for F_t. Because this process is calculated off line only once, its iterative nature does not affect simulation processing time. Notice that the calculation of the half-power beamwidth from the model parameters is still an option allowing for direct insertion of the half-power beamwidth if it is desired.

Now that we have developed and inserted the triangular shaping function into the simulation structure, we may apply it to the example case. Some experimentation revealed that a triangular weighting coefficient value of 0.6 resulted in a main-lobe shape that produced an excellent fit to the desired shape. Figure 4.10 shows the results of this triangular shaping on the original normalized power gain pattern. This pattern was created by applying only the triangular weighting to the pattern of Figure 4.5. Because we held the shaping coefficient C to its original value of 0.065, we introduced no distortion at the lobe boundaries and narrowed the main lobe's peak as desired. Notice that the use of the triangular function causes a somewhat artificial "pointing" of the main lobe. While this may appear somewhat unnatural, the mathematical fit to the desired shape is actually quite good.

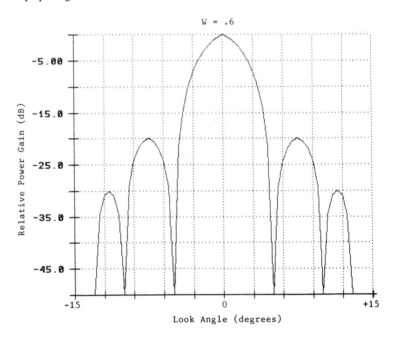

Fig. 4.10 Improved Fit with Triangular Shaping

The triangular shaping function offers the capability to adjust the shape of the antenna gain pattern near the center of a lobe without severely affecting the original shape at the lobe boundaries. This function may not be necessary for all simulation cases, but it is a valuable utility when needed.

As the value of the weighting coefficient increases beyond 1.0, the resulting lobe shape very rapidly becomes quite artificially triangular. In actual practice, it is unusual to require a weighting coefficient which exceeds a value of about 0.8. However, if this situation is encountered, it is often useful to review the original lobe coefficients. It is possible that a better choice of C, the shaping coefficient, may afford an adequate fit to the desired pattern in conjunction with a lower triangular weighting coefficient.

4.3 ANGULAR DISTORTION

In many cases, actual antennas are designed with gain patterns that are axially nonsymmetrical. That is, the antenna beamwidth is wider along one angular axis than it is along the orthogonal angular axis. Because the gain algorithm in its present state produces a gain function that is axially symmetrical, we require a modification. This modification, called *angular distortion*, permits control of the relationship between the gain pattern and its angular axes. As such, the term "distortion" refers to a constant scaling of the gain-look angle relationship along the two angular axes of the pattern, and not an irregular distortion.

The introduction of a desired amount of angular distortion is a very straight-forward process. It is simply a matter of mathematically extending or compressing the gain pattern along one or both of the angular axes, while ensuring a smooth and continuous mathematical relationship for composite angles involving components along both angular axes. This procedure is accomplished by defining some distortion coefficients and using them to adjust the angle used to interrogate the voltage gain algorithm. Assume that distortion coefficients for both angular axes are defined as follows:

D_a = azimuth distortion coefficient
D_e = elevation distortion coefficient

These distortion coefficients represent the desired percentage of distortion along the angular axes, such that a coefficient value of 100 (100%) means that no distortion is desired. In other words, the distortion coefficient describes the desired angular width of the gain pattern, relative to the undistorted pattern. For example, if the beamwidth of a particular pattern is 4° in both azimuth and elevation and we want the azimuth beamwidth to be 5°, this amount of distortion will be represented by an azimuth distortion coefficient of 125 (5 is 125% of 4). Similarly, a desired azimuth beamwidth of 3° will be represented by an azimuth distortion coefficient of 75 (3 is 75% of 4).

We introduce the angular distortion by multiplying both the azimuth and elevation components of the look angle by a factor of 100 divided by the distortion coefficient:

$$\theta_a = \theta_a \, (100/D_a)$$

$$\theta_e = \theta_e \, (100/D_e)$$

(4.21)

where

θ_a = azimuth look angle component

θ_e = elevation look angle component

D_a = azimuth distortion coefficient

D_e = elevation distortion coefficient

This process is performed *before* the composite look angle is calculated and used to drive the pattern algorithm. Thus, by reducing or increasing a component of the composite look angle by a factor proportional to the reciprocal of the distortion coefficient, we increase or decrease the angular component at which a particular gain occurs by a factor equal to the distortion coefficient. The process of calculating the composite look angle ensures a smooth and continuous mathematical relationship among the composite look angle and its azimuth and elevation components. Figure 4.11 illustrates the insertion of the angular distortion algorithm into the simulation model.

The following example demonstrates the effect of the angular distortion algorithm. Let us assume the following: the antenna gain model is structured according to Figure 4.11; the voltage gain function of Figure 4.12 is obtained with some nominal lobe coefficients; both distortion coefficients are set to a value of 100 (no distortion in either azimuth or elevation).

Without angular distortion in either angular axis, the antenna gain algorithm produces a three-dimensional voltage gain pattern that is axially symmetrical, just as it would have been before the angular distortion algorithm was added to the simulation structure. This pattern is shown in Figure 4.13.

Now, suppose that we desire a gain pattern that has the characteristics of the pattern of Figure 4.12 in the elevation axis but is 40% wider along the azimuth axis. Using lobe coefficients identical to those that produced the function in Figure 4.12 and an azimuth distortion coefficient of 140%, we produce the function illustrated in Figure 4.14. As desired, all lobes are precisely 40% wider than those of the gain pattern of Figure 4.12.

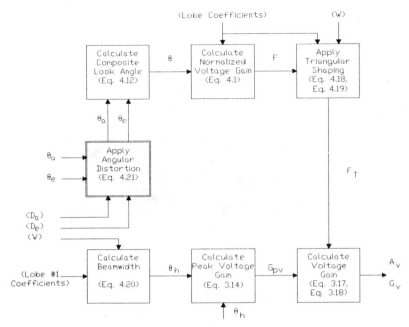

Fig. 4.11 Voltage Pattern Model with Angular Distortion

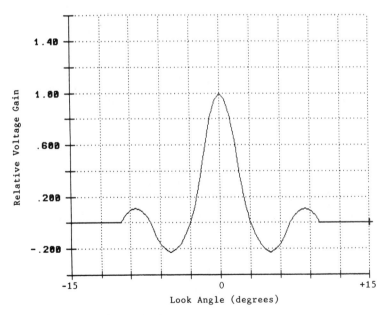

Fig. 4.12 Model-Generated Voltage Pattern

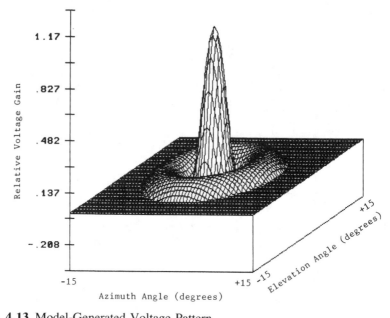

Fig. 4.13 Model-Generated Voltage Pattern

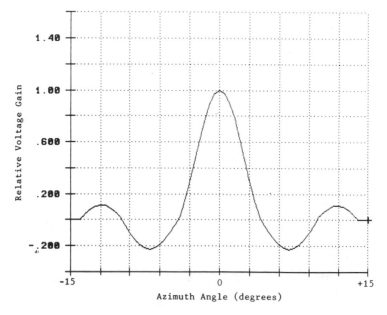

Fig. 4.14 Voltage Pattern with 140% Azimuth Distortion

The three-dimensional gain pattern resulting from this 140% azimuth distortion appears in Figure 4.15. The pattern transits smoothly and continuously from the undistorted function along the elevation axis to the mathematically widened function along the azimuth axis, which is the desired effect.

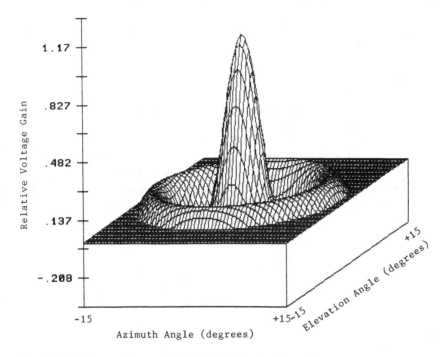

Fig. 4.15 Voltage Pattern with 140% Azimuth Distortion

The angular distortion algorithm offers a convenient and mathematically simple means for distorting or scaling the angular width of the antenna gain pattern along either or both of the angular axes, while maintaining the same relative shape and amplitude among the lobes for any radial angle.

Because we did the example case with normalized voltage gain functions, we calculated the peak gains of both the undistorted and distorted pattern to be 1.0. However, even if all other factors are equal, the undistorted pattern must have a higher actual gain than the distorted one, simply because the undistorted pattern is focusing the radiated energy into a smaller solid angle than the distorted pattern. This inequality becomes apparent through the calculation of absolute gain for each case according to the approximation of (3.13), extended to accommodate azimuth and elevation angles:

$$G_{pp} = 4\pi/(\theta_{ha}\theta_{he}) \qquad\qquad (4.22)$$

where

G_{pp} = peak power gain of the antenna
θ_{ha} = half-power azimuth beamwidth in radians
θ_{he} = half-power elevation beamwidth in radians

The half-power beamwidth for a normalized voltage gain pattern is the point at which the gain is

$$G_v = (1/2)^{0.5} = 0.707$$

Then, the angle at which the normalized voltage gain is equal to 0.707 may be read from Figure 4.12, or calculated from (3.16) or (4.20) as 2.6°. This angle represents the azimuth and elevation beamwidths for the undistorted or symmetrical case; thus, these beamwidths have a value of 2.6° or 0.0454 radians. For the distorted pattern of Figure 4.15, the elevation beamwidth is the same as that for the undistorted pattern. The azimuth beamwidth, however, is 140% wider than that for the undistorted case, which makes it equal to 3.64°, or 0.0635 radians.

The peak power gains are calculated as

$$G_{pp} = 4\pi/(0.0454)\,(0.0454) = 6096.75 \text{ (undistorted)}$$
$$G_{pp} = 4\pi/(0.0454)\,(0.0635) = 4358.93 \text{ (distorted)}$$

As expected, the distorted pattern's peak gain is less than that of the undistorted pattern by a factor equal to the reciprocal of the distortion. Stated mathematically,

$$G_{pp} = G_{pp}\,(100^2)/D_a D_e \tag{4.23}$$

$$G_{pv} = (G_{pp})^{1/2} = G_{pv}\,(100)/(D_a D_e)^{1/2} \tag{4.24}$$

where

G_{pp} = peak multiplicative power gain
G_{pv} = peak multiplicative voltage gain
D_a = azimuth distortion coefficient
D_e = elevation distortion coefficient

The point is that when we use the angular distortion algorithm to adjust the shape of a pattern, we may calculate changes in peak gain directly from the distortion coefficients and peak gain of the undistorted pattern. We need not obtain the distorted pattern beamwidths and recalculate the peak voltage gain from (3.14). Figure 4.16 illustrates the inclusion of this principle into the model.

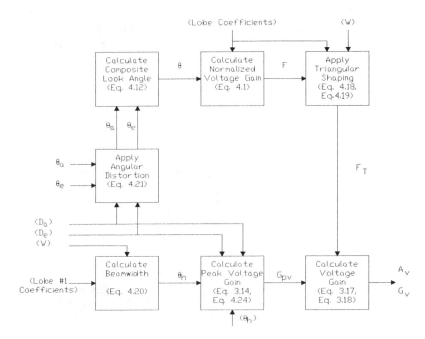

Fig. 4.16 Voltage Pattern Model with Angular Distortion

As mentioned earlier, we should note that when an actual antenna pattern is being modeled, the peak gain for the antenna is often given along with the pattern data. In this case, we may use the stated peak gain directly rather than applying any approximation based on the beamwidth. The manufacturer's data are usually based on actual measurement and are the most accurate. The beamwidth-based approximations and associated modifications for angular distortion are most valuable in conceptual or design activity, when we are making trade-off analyses among several variations in lobe shape and distortion.

4.4 RADIAL MODULATION

Up to this point, the algorithms and simulation techniques which have been developed have addressed gain purely as a function of look angle. Even the angular distortion technique developed in the preceding section, while changing the relative positions and widths of lobes in the azimuth and elevation axes, has no effect on the amplitude of these lobes as a function of radial angle.

However, actual antennas, for a variety of physical and electronic reasons, can produce gain patterns with sidelobe amplitudes that appear as a series of peaks and nulls. An example of this behavior is illustrated by the relative power gain pattern of Figure 4.17. The amplitudes of the first and second sidelobes, rather than being constant, are configured as four well defined peaks. In an actual antenna, this situation is the result of the use of a rectangular aperture, as opposed to a circular one. The series of sidelobe peaks are located between null planes forming a rectangular grid around the center of the pattern.

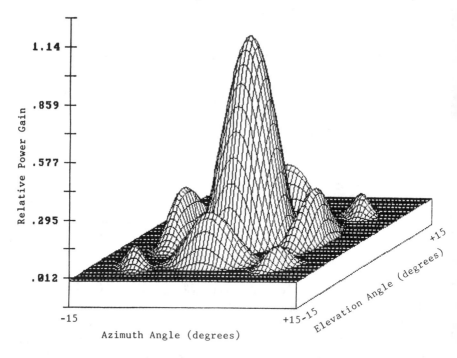

Fig. 4.17 Power Pattern with Sidelobe Amplitude Variations

Although this situation may appear rather complicated, it is really quite easy to model. Although the peaks occur in rectangles around the center of the pattern, they may be mathematically described as occurring on concentric rings around the center. Because the pattern's algorithm already produces sidelobe rings with constant amplitude, it is simply a matter of modulating these rings properly and nulling out certain peaks such that the remaining peaks occur where the rings would intercept the rectangles at the desired location of a sidelobe peak.

The process of creating the desired sidelobe peak patterns is simply that of obtaining the radial angle, then using this angle to drive a mathematical modulation function. The modulation function produces a coefficient that is multiplied by the gain obtained from the previously developed part of the simulation, resulting in the appropriate and radially varying antenna gain.

The radial angle φ is the angle of the projection of the look vector on the y-z plane with respect to the z-axis, as shown in Figure 4.18. This definition is consistent with conventions normally used in antenna analysis and design.

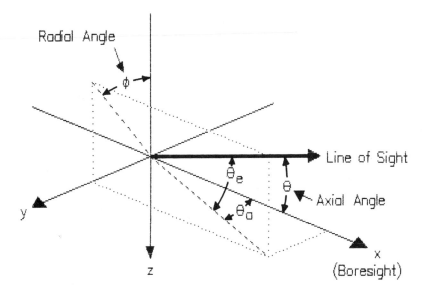

Fig. 4.18 Radial Angle in the First Quadrant

Mathematically, we can express the radial angle as a function of the positive or first-quadrant azimuth and elevation angles as follows:

$$\phi' = \tan^{-1}(\sin\theta_a/\sin\theta_e) \tag{4.25}$$

where
ϕ' = first-quadrant radial angle
θ_a = azimuth angle
θ_e = elevation angle

Unfortunately, (4.25) does not work in all quadrants, for all possible positive and negative combinations of azimuth and elevation angles. However, the situation is easily resolved by taking integer multiples of π and adding or subtracting the absolute value of the radial angle obtained from (4.24). This calculation, illustrated in Figure 4.19, results in a continuous value of the radial angle that ranges from 0 to 2π, which is precisely the value required to drive a continuous radial modulation function through the same range.

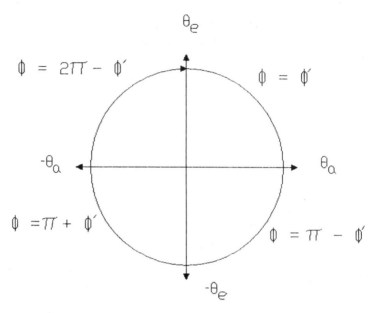

Fig. 4.19 Calculation of the Absolute Radial Angle

The appropriate calculation of ϕ is selected as a function of the combination of signs of the azimuth and elevation angles:

$$\phi = \phi' \qquad \text{when } \theta_a > 0 \text{ and } \theta_e > 0$$
$$\phi = \pi - \phi' \qquad \text{when } \theta_a > 0 \text{ and } \theta_e < 0$$
$$\phi = \pi + \phi' \qquad \text{when } \theta_a < 0 \text{ and } \theta_e < 0 \qquad (4.26)$$
$$\phi = 2\pi - \phi' \qquad \text{when } \theta_a < 0 \text{ and } \theta_e > 0$$

The radial modulation function needs to be flexible enough to allow the user to define the number of amplitude peaks and their (radial) angular widths for each sidelobe. A useful algorithm may be derived from a simple cosine function:

$$f(\phi) = \cos\phi$$

where

$\quad f(\phi)$ = function being derived
$\quad \phi \quad$ = radial angle

This function, of course, produces one cycle of a cosine function for a range of the radial angle, ϕ, from 0 to 2π. Now, because we wish to select a number of cycles, we may multiply the cosine function by an integer representing the desired number of cycles, N_c, which results in a function that produces N_c cosine cycles for a radial angle range from 0 to 2π:

$$f(\phi) = \cos(N_c\phi)$$

As it now stands, the function is at a maximum value of 1.0 when $\phi = 0$. It would be useful to have the ability to adjust the starting point of the function to some point in the cycle other than its maximum at $\phi = 0$. We can adjust this point by adding an offset term to the argument of the cosine function, which is essentially a phase shift of the modulation function. We can mathematically structure the phase shift as a multiplicative coefficient P_c of π as a convenient means of formulating this term:

$$f(\phi) = \cos(N_c\phi + P_c\pi)$$

For functional shaping reasons, we want the function to be a cosine function in the power domain. Therefore, the function must be the square root of a cosine in the voltage domain. Because the cosine function may have a positive or negative sign, we need to take its absolute value, determine the square root, then restore the sign:

$$f(\phi) = S_g|\cos(N_c\phi + P_c\pi)|^{1/2}$$

where
$$S_g = +1 \quad \text{if } \cos(N_c\phi + P_c\pi) > 0$$
$$S_g = -1 \quad \text{if } \cos(N_c\phi + P_c\pi) < 0$$

Next, because the radial modulation is to be a multiplicative coefficient of gain, the function must be normalized to a range of 0 to 1.0. We normalize the function simply by dividing it by 2.0 and adding a value of 0.5:

$$f(\phi) = |\cos(N_c\phi + P_c\pi)|^{1/2}/2.0 + 0.5$$

We then wish to consider shaping of the peaks created by this modulation function. Recall that we devoted considerable effort to deriving the exponential and triangular shaping algorithms used for shaping the lobes. This was done because lobe shape as a function of θ, the composite look angle, is a critical factor to the radar tracking process, especially in the main lobe. However, the shape of sidelobes as a function of the radial angle is not as critical. In fact, the amplitude and location of the peaks within a sidelobe are usually far more important than the shape of these peaks. Consequently, the shape of the radial modulation function may be left as simply that of the cosine function for the relative decimal power gain situation, and as the square root of the cosine function for the relative decimal voltage gain situation.

In certain cases, we may wish to modulate only a part of the sidelobe amplitude. Therefore, we must make the modulation function operate over a selected percentage of the amplitude. In order to accommodate this, we define a modulation percentage coefficient, P_m, as the percentage of the sidelobe voltage gain amplitude over which the radial modulation function applies. This modulation percentage, in classical fashion, is applied mathematically to the radial modulation function as follows:

$$f'(\phi) = \left[f(\phi)P_m + 100 - P_m \right] /100$$

Thus, a modulation percentage of 40%, for example, results in the modulation function operating between the values of 0.6 and 1.0. By assigning a modulation percentage greater than 100%, the function can create cyclic, radial zero crossings. This effect is quite valuable in creating cross-polarized gain patterns, as discussed in the next chapter.

If a modeler constructs a mathematical model of an antenna using the radial modulation function, he or she may wish to use only selected peaks within a sidelobe rather than every possible peak. Therefore, a peak numbering system is required so that the modeler may select certain peaks to be omitted or blanked. The following functions use the argument of the cosine function from the radial modulation expression to assign sequentially a peak number, N_p, to each peak within a sidelobe with increasing values of the radial angle.

$$N_p = \text{int} \left[\frac{N_c\phi + P_c\pi}{2\pi} + 0.5 \right]$$

where int is the integer of the argument and N_p is set equal to N_c when N_p is calculated to be 0.0.

Finally, the radial modulation algorithm may be summarized as follows:

$$R_m = [f(\phi)P_m + 100 - P_m] /100 \tag{4.27}$$

$$N_p = \text{int} \left[\frac{N_c\phi + P_c\pi}{2\pi} + 0.5 \right] \tag{4.28}$$

(Set N_p to N_c when $N_p = 0$)

(Set R_m to 0.0 when $N_p = $ any N_b)

where
R_m = radial modulation coefficient, a multiplier of voltage gain
N_c = number of radial modulation cycles
P_c = radial modulation cosine function's phase shift coefficient
P_m = modulation percentage
N_p = peak number, an identifier
N_b = a peak number to be blanked
ϕ = radial angle in radians
$f(\phi) = |\cos(N_c\phi + P_c\pi)|^{1/2}/2.0 + 0.5$

The radial modulation coefficient is simply multiplied by the multiplicative voltage gain to produce the radially modulated voltage gain:

$$F_m = R_m F \tag{4.29}$$

where
F_m = radially modulated multiplicative voltage gain
F = multiplicative voltage gain (with or without triangular shaping)

Figure 4.20 illustrates the effects of several combinations of cycle counts, phase shift coefficients, and modulation percentages. The circles denote the axial angular boundaries of the sidelobe, and the radial lines show the radial angular boundaries of the peaks in the sidelobe with the peak number indicated in these boundaries.

This technique of locating and bounding peaks within sidelobes may appear to be somewhat restricted in its capability to locate these peaks precisely. A more precise technique would be to define specifically the radial angular boundaries of each peak. However, the goal of these algorithms is not ultimate accuracy. Rather, we strive for adequate accuracy within the bounds of computational simplicity. Most antennas are physically symmetrical devices that exhibit electronically symmetrical gain patterns within each of the orthogonal angular axes. It is in the modeler's interest to take advantage of this symmetry in the development of fundamental algorithms and use scaling factors for special cases when they arise.

The radial modulation algorithm, consisting of (4.26) and (4.27), allows us to define as many peaks as desired for a particular sidelobe through only four coefficients. However, defining each peak individually would require us to define two radial angular boundaries for each peak—an unnecessary increase in complexity.

Figure 4.21 illustrates how the radial modulation algorithm is incorporated into the simulation model. The use of this enhancement to the model can be demonstrated through an example.

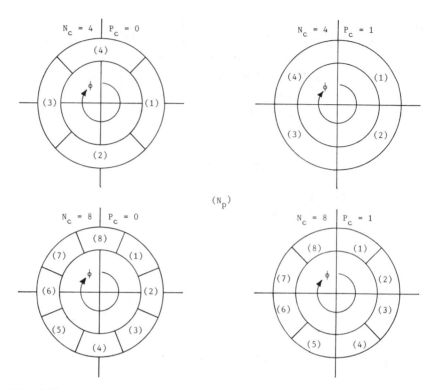

Fig. 4.20 Combinations of Cycle Count (N_c) and Phase Shift (P_c)

Suppose we want the normalized decimal power gain pattern of Figure 4.22. This type of pattern could very well be that of a rectangular planar array with a small number of individual elements. As the number of elements in an array increases, the gain pattern approaches that of a continuous aperture that exhibits sidelobes of more or less constant radial amplitude. The process of creating this pattern is simply that of defining the axial lobe coefficients for the peaks of the sidelobes, then working out the radial modulation.

For this example, let us assume that we know the lobe coefficients for the sidelobes. The process of actually extracting these coefficients from a three-dimensional pattern such as that of Figure 4.22 will be discussed in the subsequent chapters, which deal with using the model to simulate various actual antenna patterns. Figure 4.23 illustrates the desired pattern before application of the radial modulation technique. To create the desired pattern, the first sidelobe must be divided into four peaks with no angular separation between them, and the second sidelobe must be divided into four peaks with some angular separation between them.

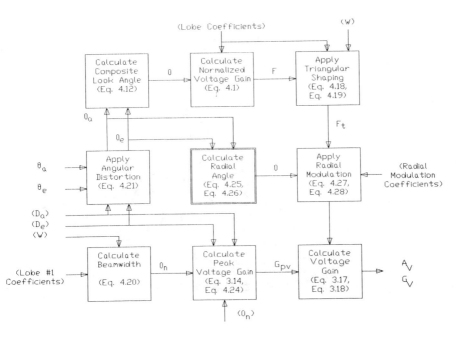

Fig. 4.21 Voltage Pattern Model with Radial Modulation

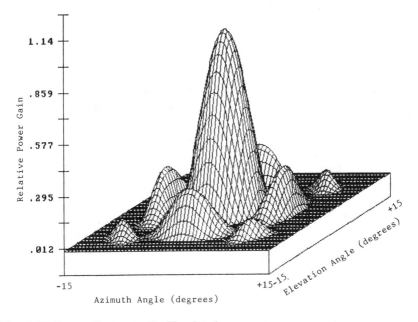

Fig. 4.22 Power Pattern to Be Simulated

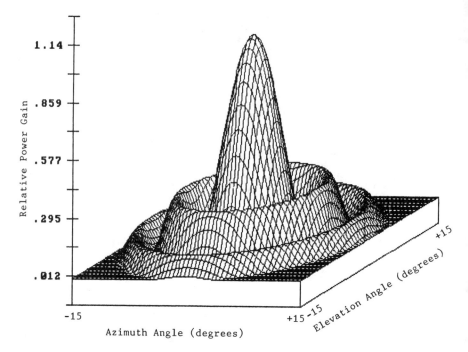

Fig. 4.23 Model-Generated Pattern with No Added Radial Modulation

     Let us begin with the first sidelobe. Because the peaks must occur continuously with no angular separation, the number of radial modulation cycles is equal to the desired number of peaks, which is four. Thus, the cycle number coefficient is 4.0. According to the derivation of the radial modulation function described earlier in this section, we must also select a phase shift coefficient. The centers of the peaks are to be located on the azimuth and elevation axes of the pattern, which occur at radial angles of 0, $\pi/2$, π, and $3\pi/2$ radians. With four cycles, the radial modulation cosine function is at maximum at these angles, which means that the function does not require any phase shift for this application. Because the phase shift coefficient is a multiplier of π, its value must be 0.0. The minimum amplitude of the peaks is 0.0. Therefore, the modulation percentage coefficient is 100, representing 100%. Figure 4.24 shows the result of applying radial modulation with the coefficients determined above to the first sidelobe of the pattern of Figure 4.23.

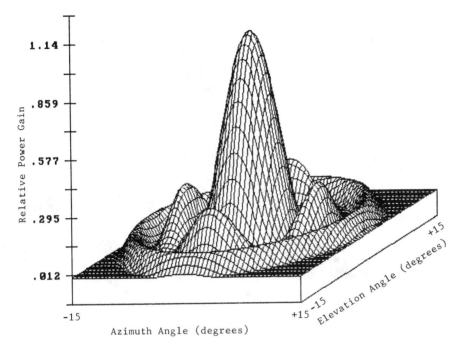

Fig. 4.24 Radial Modulation Added to the First Sidelobe

The second sidelobe also has four peaks, but unlike the first sidelobe, there is some angular spacing between these peaks. This situation may be accommodated simply by selecting the number of cycles to be greater than four, and selectively blanking peaks that are not desired. In this case, selecting a cycle number coefficient of 12.0 results in the desired radial angular width for the peaks. Also, because use of this coefficient results in three cosine zeros between each azimuth and elevation axis, a zero is located precisely halfway between these axes. This point is the desired radial location for the peak, not the zero. Thus, a phase shift of π is required, making the phase shift coefficient equal to 1.0. As with the first sidelobe, the minimum voltage gain is 0.0, requiring a modulation percentage coefficient of 100. Using the previously described peak-numbering algorithm, the peaks to be used are numbers 2, 5, 8, and 11. Therefore, all other peaks are blanked, resulting in the desired pattern of Figure 4.25.

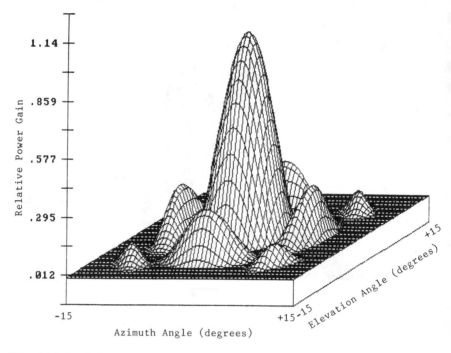

Fig. 4.25 Radial Modulation Added to Both Sidelobes

4.5 SUMMARY

In this chapter, we extended the capabilities of the basic antenna voltage pattern model in three areas. First, we added a triangular shaping function to give the user more precise control of the lobe shape in critical areas. Next, we included an angular distortion algorithm, which allowed the user to create gain patterns that were not constrained to be symmetrical in azimuth and elevation. Finally, we incorporated a radial modulation function, providing the user with a means to modulate selectively the amplitude of the sidelobes of the gain pattern.

At this point, the antenna model is fairly well developed. Computationally, its algorithms and functions are quite easy to use. The model is ready to be applied to the task of modeling some realistic antenna patterns.

Chapter 5
Application to Horn and Reflector Antennas

This chapter introduces the process of applying the antenna voltage pattern model, developed in the previous chapters, to the task of modeling horn and reflector antennas. Actually, the methods described in this chapter are applicable to many other types of antennas, but horn and reflector antennas are typically found in a radar system. A third type of radar antenna, the planar array, requires some enhancements to the simulation in order to be modeled and is the subject of Chapter 6.

Ideally, when modeling the antenna pattern, we ought to have numerical data or some graphical description of the three-dimensional pattern as well as the absolute gain at boresight. Although this kind of detailed information is sometimes available, in most cases the amount and accuracy of the data are considerably less than ideal. Hence, the modeler must make some assumptions and draw some conclusions when configuring the parameters for the antenna gain model.

The examples given in this chapter represent cases for which we must develop models based on diverse sets of known and unknown antenna parameters. The conditions, choices, and decisions presented here are quite typical of those which would confront a modeler in an actual simulation design.

5.1 MODELING A KNOWN ANTENNA PATTERN

When the gain pattern of an antenna to be modeled is known, it is usually from one of the following sources:

- Theoretical derivations;
- Manufacturer's specifications;
- Measured data.

If the source is a theoretical derivation, a three-dimensional pattern will sometimes be available. This type of pattern, such as that of Figure 5.1, may look impressive but does not allow easy extraction of numerical information.

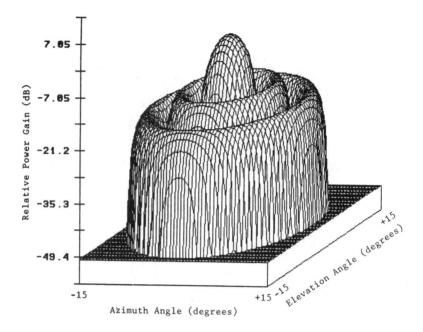

Fig. 5.1 Typical Three-Dimensional Normalized Power Pattern

Recall that the basic coefficients required for each antenna pattern lobe in the voltage gain model are as follows:

θ_l = lower angular boundary
θ_u = upper angular boundary
M = maximum lobe gain in dB voltage gain
C = shaping coefficient
D_a, D_e = angular distortion coefficients
W = triangular weighting coefficient
SL = algebraic sign (or phase shift)

When radial modulation is required, we add the following lobe coefficients:

N_c = the number of radial modulation cycles
P_c = the cosine function's phase shift coefficient
N_b = the cycle numbers of cycles to be nulled
P_m = the modulation percentage

We can extract the angular boundaries and maximum lobe gains to some degree of accuracy by using the graphical techniques shown in Figure 5.2. Because the angular boundaries differ in azimuth and elevation, we use the angular distortion coefficient to scale the boundaries that have a wider separation along one axis to those of the other axis. Because the pattern given is in dB, which is typical, we must convert the interpreted values of maximum lobe gain to dBvg.

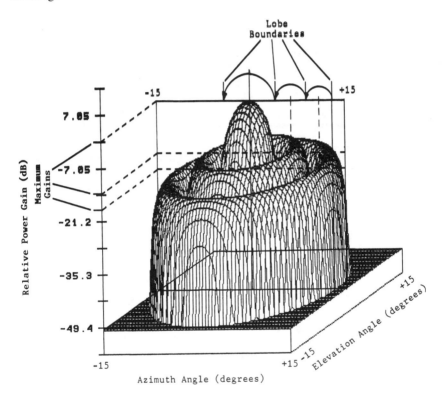

Fig. 5.2 Graphical Extraction of Lobe Data

Once these parameters have been interpreted, the next step is to apply them to the gain model along with some nominal values for the shaping and triangular weighting coefficients. Then, through some iterative trial and error, we may produce antenna gain patterns by the model and qualitatively compare them to the given pattern to achieve a reasonable fit. The key phrase here is ''reasonable fit'' because there is little use in spending a great deal of time trying to get a precise match for data that are in such a qualitative state.

In the absence of information to the contrary, we can reasonably presume that the phase shift or mathematical signs of the lobes follow the normal convention. Recall from Chapter 3 that this convention assigns a positive sign and no phase shift to the main or first lobe, and progressively alternates this parameter with the lobe number, as shown in Table 5.1.

Table 5.1

Lobe Number	Sign	Phase Shift (Degrees)
1	+	0
2	−	180
3	+	0

If the antenna pattern information is from the manufacturer's specifications or measured data, then a three-dimensional pattern is usually not given. Rather, if a pattern is given at all, it is typically presented in the form of a normalized power gain as a function of azimuth and elevation angle. A typical pattern for a parabolic reflector antenna could appear as shown in Figure 5.3.

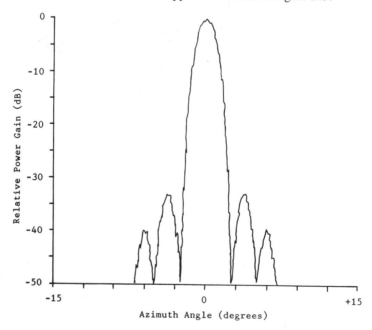

Fig. 5.3(a) Example of a Parabolic Reflector Azimuth Pattern

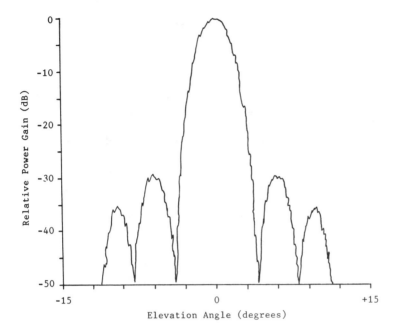

Fig. 5.3(b) Example of a Parabolic Reflector Elevation Pattern

Notice that both azimuth and elevation normalized power patterns are given. In order to configure the antenna pattern model to these data, we need some interpretation of the graphical data.

We must first establish the angular boundaries of the lobes, which are the mathematical zero crossings of the gain pattern or the angular points at which the gain pattern exhibits relative minima. A comparison of these points for the two gain patterns of Figure 5.3 is given in Table 5.2.

The data of Table 5.2 show that the angular placement of the lobes along one axis is related to the angular placement along the other axis by a fairly constant ratio. This means that the zeros for one axis may be used to define the lobe boundaries for the model, and the distortion along the other axis can be handled with the angular distortion percentage. This results in the definition of the coefficients for the model, which are given in Table 5.3.

Notice that the positive and negative zero-crossing points along either axis were quite similar in both the positive and negative direction, and average values were assigned for the lobe boundaries. This is typically true, and the technique of averaging will work in the majority of cases. However, it is possible to encounter a pattern in which the lobe boundaries in the positive direction differ from those in the negative direction. We can handle these rare instances simply by assigning different distortion coefficients for each direction along each axis.

Table 5.2

Azimuth Zeros (Degrees)	Elevation Zeros (Degrees)	Ratio (EL/AZ)
−7.0	−11.1	1.59
−5.0	−7.9	1.58
−2.5	−4.0	1.60
2.5	4.0	1.60
5.1	8.0	1.60
6.9	11.0	1.59

Note: average ratio = 1.59

Table 5.3

Lobe Number (N)	Lower Boundary $\theta_l(N)$ (Degrees)	Upper Boundary $\theta_u(N)$ (Degrees)
1	−2.5	2.5
2	2.5	5.0
3	5.0	6.9

Azimuth Distortion: $D_a = 100\%$
Elevation Distortion: $D_e = 159\%$

Returning to the situation at hand, the next step is to assign maximum gain values to the lobes. The data are interpreted in Table 5.4 from the patterns of Figure 5.3.

Because the gain values for each direction along a particular axis are quite similar, they may be averaged and then divided by two to obtain the desired maximum gains in dBvg. The resulting data are shown in Table 5.5.

Table 5.4

Lobe Number	Direction (+ or −)	Azimuth Gain (dB)	Elevation Gain (dB)
3	−	− 40	− 36
2	−	− 33	− 29
1		0	0
2	+	− 32	− 30
3	+	− 39	− 35

Table 5.5

Lobe Number	Azimuth Gain (dBvg)	Elevation Gain (dBvg)
1	0	0
2	− 16.25	− 14.75
3	− 19.75	− 17.75

The data of Table 5.5 indicate that the gain along the azimuth axis is somewhat less than the gain along the elevation axis. The model can accommodate this situation through its radial modulation technique. Recall from Chapter 4 that this technique allows us to define a certain number of modulation cycles as a function of radial angle. For this case, specification of two modulation cycles with a modulation phase shift of 0.0 creates the desired condition, illustrated in Figure 5.4, in which the modulation amplitude peaks at the elevation axis and minimizes at the azimuth axis.

We still must define two more parameters: the maximum dB voltage gains and modulation percentages for the two sidelobes. Because the radial modulation will handle the differences in maximum gain between the azimuth and elevation axes, the maximum gain values to be used are simply the greater of the values for the two axes. In this example, these are the values along the elevation axis: − 14.75 dBvg for lobe 2 and − 17.75 dBvg for lobe 3. The modulation percentages are calculated as the ratio of maximum to minimum dBvg values within the lobe, subtracted from 1.0 and expressed as a percentage:

$$P_m = \left[1 - 10^{|A_{vx} - A_{vn}|/10} \right] 100 \qquad (5.1)$$

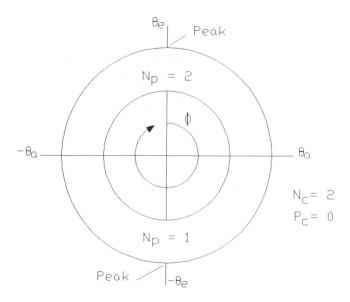

Fig. 5.4 Radial Modulation Applied to the Simulation Requirement

where

P_m = modulation percentage
A_{vx} = maximum dB voltage gain
A_{vn} = minimum dB voltage gain

Application of (5.1) to the dBvg values interpreted from the graphs of Figure 5.3 results in the calculation of modulation percentages of 29.2 and 36.9, respectively, for lobes 2 and 3. This results in the definition of the coefficients of Table 5.6.

Table 5.6

Lobe Number (N)	Maximum dBvg M(N)	Modulation Cycles $N_c(N)$	Phase Shift $P_c(N)$	Modulation Percentage $P_m(N)$
1	0	0	—	—
2	− 14.75	2	0	29.2
3	− 16.75	2	0	36.9

Two additional parameters to be defined for the gain model are the exponential shaping and triangular shaping coefficients. In order to set up a model, the best procedure is to start with some nominal values for the exponential shaping coefficient between 0.04 and 0.10, and to attempt to fit the desired pattern's lobe shapes through some iterative modification. At this point, it is most convenient to have the model implemented in software with access to a good plotting utility. If we obtain a reasonable fit by using the exponential shaping coefficient, we need not use the triangular shaping technique. For the case at hand, a good fit was obtained by using the shaping coefficients found in Table 5.7.

Table 5.7

Lobe Number (N)	Shaping Coefficient C(N)	Triangular Weighting W(N)
1	0.1	0
2	0.06	0
3	0.045	0

The final parameter to be defined is the phase shift, or sign of the lobes. In the absence of specific data, we assume the standard convention, which results in the values given by Table 5.8.

Table 5.8

Lobe Number (N)	Sign S(N)	Phase Shift (Degrees)
1	+	0
2	−	180
3	+	0

We have now fitted the model to the data of Figure 5.3. The results of the fitting process are shown in Figure 5.5, which compares well with the original data. We did not attempt to model the small variations of the original patterns. These fluctuations, probably due to the imperfections of real hardware or noise in the measurement system, are usually not germane to a simulation. If it is

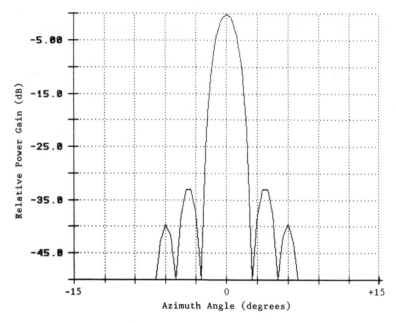

Fig. 5.5(a) Model-Generated Fit to Parabolic Reflector's Azimuth Pattern

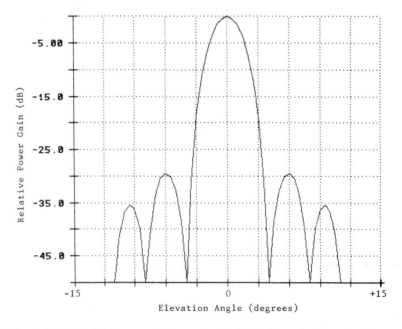

Fig. 5.5(b) Model-Generated Fit to Parabolic Reflector's Elevation Pattern

necessary to model these variations, a normally distributed random variable of some nominal mean and variance can be added to the decimal voltage gain values to represent this effect.

Now that we have determined the parameters for the gain model, the model will calculate a relative voltage gain or power gain as a function of the azimuth and elevation angles. However, in order to calculate the absolute gain, we must specify the peak gain of the antenna. If the source of the original gain patterns is a manufacturer, the peak gain will usually be given. If not, it is reasonable to use the approximation described in (4.22) to calculate this parameter. For the case at hand, the following information may be interpreted from the graphical data of Figure 5.3:

> Azimuth beamwidth = 1.7° (0.030 radians)
> Elevation beamwidth = 2.8° (0.049 radians)

As an alternative approach, we may calculate the beamwidths from the modeling function, which was fitted to the graphical data by solving (4.20) for θ with M set to -4.5 dBvg:

$$-6.0 = \left\{ \sin\left[\left(\frac{\theta + 2.5}{5.0}\right)\pi\right] \right\}^{0.1} (95.5) - 100 \quad \text{from (4.20)}$$

and

$$\theta_h = 2\theta = 2(0.87) = 1.74°$$

> Azimuth beamwidth = $\theta_h D_a/100$ = 1.74° (0.030 radians)
> Elevation beamwidth = $\theta_h D_e/100$ = 2.77° (0.048 radians)

Regardless of the means used to determine the beamwidth, the peak gain is calculated as

$$G_{pp} = \frac{4\pi}{\theta_{ha}\theta_{he}} = \frac{4\pi}{(0.030)(0.048)} = 8727 \quad \text{(from (4.22))}$$
$$G_{pv} = (G_{pp})^{1/2} = 93.42$$
$$A_{pv} = 10 \log (G_{pv}) = 19.7 \text{ dBvg}$$

We then add this peak dB voltage gain to the normalized dBvg value to produce the absolute gain in dBvg. We may then convert to decimal voltage gain, dB power gain, or decimal power gain as required.

From this example, it is apparent that the process of modeling a known antenna pattern is quite straightforward. We extract data from the given graphical and numerical information to the best accuracy possible, and mathematically transform them into coefficients for the gain model. Lobe shaping is generally the least quantified parameter and is consequently subject to some iterative changing in the process of achieving the desired fit. However, once the coefficients have been determined, the model will execute rapidly in the simulation, regardless of the particular software language in which it is structured.

5.2   MODELING AN UNKNOWN ANTENNA PATTERN

In certain instances, it may be necessary to produce an antenna model without the benefit of specific knowledge of the gain pattern. Often, we know only the beamwidth, and perhaps a stated sidelobe level for the first few sidelobes. When this is the case, we look to the fairly prevalent modeling philosophy, which says:

"When in doubt, use the sinc function!"

However, even if we know only the beamwidth and sidelobe levels, we may draw some reasonable analogies to other known patterns to obtain a considerably better representation than the sinc (sinx/x) function. Therefore, a better philosophy of modeling is

"When in doubt, look for analogous patterns.
If none can be found, use the sinc function."

Many sources for analogous patterns are available, including manufacturer's data and test data. Additionally, we find an excellent reference for theoretical gain functions in the appendix to *Handbook of Radar Measurement* by David K. Barton and Harold R. Ward (Artech House, 1984). This appendix gives patterns for a wide variety of illumination functions. However, the modeler needs to be able to relate the function type to the antenna of interest.

Regardless of the source, having selected a suitable analog, which should be more suitable than the sinc function, we may then relate the known pattern to the known parameters of the antenna to be modeled. The following example illustrates this technique. Assume a gain model is desired for an antenna with the following known characteristics:

Antenna Type:	Parabolic Reflector
Beamwidth (-3 dB):	2.4°
Sidelobe Levels:	First . . . -15 dB
	Second . . . -20 dB

This information is obviously pretty sketchy, but it is still usable. The first step is to find a good analogous pattern. Recall that the example given in Section 5.1 fitted the pattern model to a parabolic reflector antenna. This is precisely the type of antenna being modeled in our example here, so its gain pattern is an excellent analog for the present application.

Normally, the next step would be to model the analogous pattern. The entire process consists of modeling and scaling, and the modeling should be done first in order to fit the known analogous pattern. In this case, the modeling was already accomplished in the example of the previous section. The results obtained earlier are presented again in Figure 5.6.

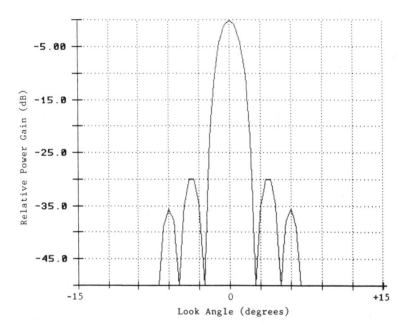

Fig. 5.6 Analogous Pattern

The next step is to scale the angular positions of the lobes to achieve the desired beamwidth. Because the desired beamwidth is 2.4° and the beamwidth of the analogous pattern is 1.7°, the scaling factor is

2.4/1.7 = 1.41

This scaling factor may be applied by multiplying the lower and upper angular boundary coefficients of the analogous pattern by 1.41. However, we can apply this factor more easily by setting the angular distortion percentage to 141%. Either method will work, and the result is the pattern of Figure 5.7. Because only a single beamwidth was given, we may presume that it is applicable to both the azimuth and elevation axes, requiring equivalent angular distortion coefficients for both axes.

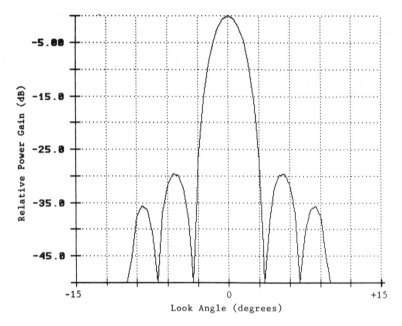

Fig. 5.7 Analogous Pattern Extended to Proper Beamwidth

If no sidelobe data were given, it would be reasonable to leave the sidelobe amplitudes as they are in the analogous pattern. However, in this case, sidelobe levels were given, so the final step is that of applying them to the pattern. Because these levels were given as power gain quantities in dB, we can determine the appropriate maximum dBvg values for the gain model by simply dividing the levels in half, as shown in Table 5.9.

Table 5.9

Lobe Number (N)	Given Sidelobe Level (dB)	Maximum Gain M(N) (dBvg)
1	—	0.0
2	-15	-7.5
3	-20	-10.0

Replacing the maximum dBvg values of the scaled analogous pattern with those calculated from the given data results in the relative power gain pattern of Figure 5.8. This pattern shows the effects of both the angular scaling and gain scaling on the original analogous pattern.

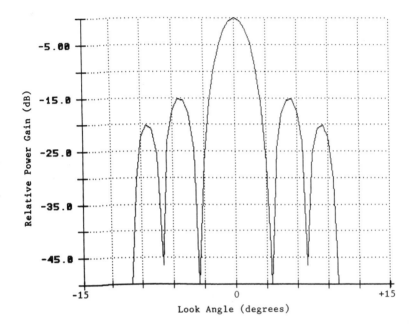

Fig. 5.8 Analogous Pattern with Proper Sidelobe Levels

In a case such as this, where we had no explicit information pertaining to the shape of the sidelobes, we usually do not need to make an adjustment to the lobe shaping coefficients obtained from the analogous pattern. In other words, if the shape of the sidelobes were important to the simulation, it should have been defined. However, we can reasonably assume that the transition from lobe to lobe is smooth and continuous in the decimal voltage gain domain. This expectation may be assessed by investigating the normalized voltage gain pattern shown in Figure 5.9.

The voltage gain pattern of Figure 5.9 shows that the gain function transits quite smoothly between the first and second sidelobes. However, the transition between the main lobe and the first sidelobe shows an abrupt change in slope at the zero crossing. The situation may be remedied by adjusting the shape of either the first sidelobe or the main lobe. However, because an adjustment to the first sidelobe could disturb the acceptable transition between the first and second sidelobes, we must make the adjustment to the main lobe.

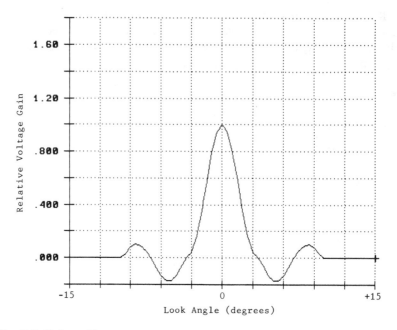

Fig. 5.9 Voltage Pattern

We make this adjustment by reducing the value of the lobe shape coefficient for the main lobe. A reduction from the present value of 0.10 to a value of 0.08 accomplishes the desired smoothing of the voltage gain function, as Figure 5.10 illustrates.

If the adjustment had been made to a sidelobe, the modeling process would be complete at this point and the pattern of Figure 5.10 would be acceptable. However, because we adjusted the shape of the main lobe, we also changed the beamwidth, which is no longer the desired value of 2.4°. This situation may be remedied by a final adjustment to the angular distortion coefficients to compensate for the change in shape. With the new shape coefficient value, we may calculate the beamwidth according to (4.20) as

$$-6.0 = \left\{ \sin \left[\left(\frac{\theta + 2.5(1.41)}{5.0(1.41)} \right) \pi \right] \right\}^{0.08} (95.5) - 100$$

$$\theta_h = 2\theta = 2.7°$$

We may achieve the desired beamwidth of 2.4° by simply multiplying the present angular distortion coefficients by the ratio of the desired beamwidth to

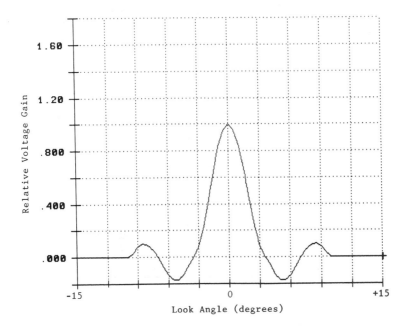

Fig. 5.10 Voltage Pattern Showing Adjustment to Main Lobe Shape

the present beamwidth. This calculation results in new angular distortion coefficients for both axes:

$$D_a = D_e = 141(2.4/2.7) = 125.33$$

This final modification results in the voltage and power gain patterns of Figure 5.11. These patterns show that the modeled function has the desired beamwidth, sidelobe levels, and lobe-to-lobe functional transition for the specified antenna.

The modeling example presented here shows how we may produce a suitable antenna gain pattern, even when the given information is quite sketchy. The technique of fitting an analogous antenna pattern to the desired characteristics is a valid method, which will produce acceptable results. Obviously, the more sample patterns a modeler has, the better the chances are of obtaining a good analogous pattern. The prudent modeler will strive to accumulate a diversified library of antenna patterns from manufacturers' specifications, test data, theoretical derivations, and previously modeled patterns.

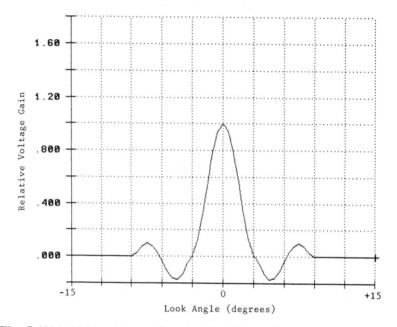

Fig. 5.11(a) Voltage Pattern Showing Final Beamwidth Adjustment

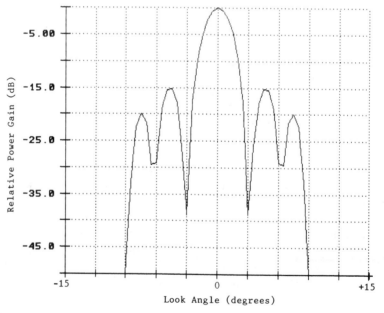

Fig. 5.11(b) Power Pattern Showing Final Beamwidth Adjustment

5.3   MODELING THE CROSS-POLARIZED GAIN PATTERN

In Chapter 2, we pointed out that under certain modeling conditions, it is necessary to model the pattern of an antenna in the polarization orthogonal to the principal polarization. This is often referred to as the cross-polarized pattern.

The characteristics of the cross-polarized pattern of a given antenna differ considerably from those of the normal, or co-polarized, pattern. The predominant characteristics of the cross-polarized gain pattern of parabolic reflector antennas are as follows:

- The pattern exhibits a zero crossing rather than a peak amplitude at boresight.
- The peak gain of the pattern occurs in four lobes located approximately at radial angles of 45°, 135°, 225°, and 315°.
- The peak gain of these four lobes, often called *Condon lobes*, is usually at least 20 dB lower than the peak gain of the co-polarized pattern.

Information describing the cross-polarized gain characteristics of a given antenna is generally not available in open literature. However, when we can obtain this information, we may fit the gain model to it as easily as to that of a co-polarized antenna. The process is identical to that described earlier in this chapter, which is simply that of establishing lobe boundaries, maximum gains, shaping coefficients, and radial modulation coefficients. For example, Figure 5.12 shows representative co-polarized and cross-polarized power gain patterns for some hypothetical parabolic antennas.

The cross-polarized pattern of Figure 5.12 was created using the following voltage pattern model coefficients:

$$\theta_l \;=\; 0°$$
$$\theta_u \;=\; 9°$$
$$M \;=\; -10 \text{ dBvg}$$
$$C \;=\; 0.045$$
$$W \;=\; 0 \text{ (no triangular shaping)}$$
$$D_a \;=\; 100\% \text{ (no azimuth distortion)}$$
$$D_e \;=\; 100\% \text{ (no elevation distortion)}$$
$$N_c \;=\; 2 \text{ cycles (2 maxima + 2 minima = 4 lobes)}$$
$$P_c \;=\; 0.5 \text{ (lobe extrema at } \pi/4 = 45° \text{ intervals)}$$
$$P_m \;=\; 200\% \text{ (zero crossings desired)}$$
$$N_b \;=\; 0 \text{ (no blanked cycles)}$$

For the first time, we needed to assign a modulation percentage of more than 100% to produce zero crossings within the radial modulation function. The cross-polarized situation is the one for which this capability was designed, and

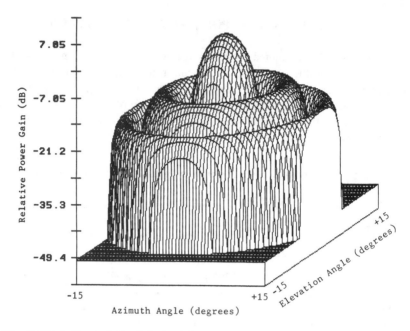

Fig. 5.12(a) Typical Co-Polarized Power Pattern

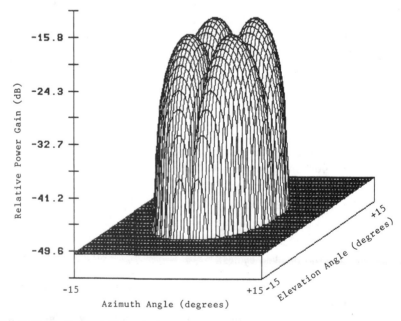

Fig. 5.12(b) Typical Cross-Polarized Power Pattern

it is typically not necessary for the co-polarized situation. The effect of these zero crossings is not apparent in the relative power gain pattern, but we can readily observe the effect in the relative voltage gain pattern of Figure 5.13.

In this example, the cross-polarized gain was modeled such that the amplitudes were relative to the co-polarized gain. This allows the co-polarized peak gain to be used with the cross-polarized relative gain from the model to calculate the cross-polarized absolute gain:

$$A_{vx} = A_{pv} + A'_{vx}$$

where x denotes the cross-polarized component.

As we modeled the cross-polarized gain pattern, we made no effort to model any secondary lobes besides the four Condon lobes. This is typical of most simulation requirements because the cross-polarized sidelobe gain is quite small, relative to the co-polarized gain. However, the secondary lobes may be similarly modeled if we know their characteristics, and these lobes are significant to the simulation requirements.

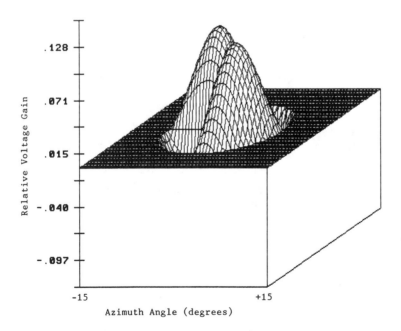

Fig. 5.13 Voltage Gain Version of the Cross-Polarized Pattern

5.4 SUMMARY

In this chapter, we applied the antenna gain model to the modeling of several example antenna patterns with varying levels of parameter definition. The techniques discussed here apply to the modeling of horn and reflector types of antennas, and demonstrate the capabilities of the model to handle both co-polarized and cross-polarized gain patterns. The examples showed a logical and orderly approach to configuring the model, based on the level of definition available for the antenna being modeled. However, as is the case with most tools, the best teacher is experience, and the modeler will become quite adept at antenna modeling with a little practice.

Chapter 6
Application to Planar Array Antennas

In this chapter, we apply the voltage pattern model to the simulation of planar array antennas. This type of antenna differs physically and electronically from simpler antennas such as horn and illuminated reflectors, and these differences result in gain behavior that requires an addition to the model.

Some typical planar array configurations are illustrated in Figure 6.1. Notice that the shape of the array can be circular, rectangular, or any geometric shape desired. The array is composed of many small, similar antennas or antenna elements. By controlling the geometric properties of the array, such as element size, orientation, and spacing, and the electrical current distribution across the elements, we may achieve almost any desired pattern. In a sense, we create a large effective aperture by configuring an array of significant area. Then, by driving a large number of elements with similar and progressively phase-shifted currents, we approach the effect of a uniformly illuminated, continuous aperture.

In practical terms, the phased array will exhibit gain and pattern behavior that is somewhat different from that of an ideal continuous aperture. As the area of the array increases, the beamwidth of the main lobe decreases because the beamwidth varies inversely with aperture size. This is usually a desirable effect for a tracking radar. However, this increase in area causes the number of sidelobes to increase. If the array is arranged as a circular aperture, the amplitude of these sidelobes will be constant at any radial angle. However, an array configured as a noncircular aperture (rectangular, for example) will produce sidelobes with amplitude variations, which may be simulated with cyclic amplitude modulation as a function of radial angle, as we discussed in Chapter 4.

Another feature of the planar array, in addition to being capable of narrow beamwidth, is that of electronically controlled directivity, often called *electronic pointing* or *steering*. Normally, the maximum gain of an array's main lobe occurs at boresight, where both azimuth and elevation angles are equal to 0.0. By altering the progressive phase shifts among the elements, we may control the far-field wave interference phenomena such that the main lobe's peak gain is pointed, or steered, to some other angle.

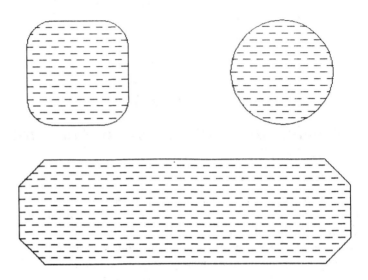

Fig. 6.1 Examples of Planar Array Shapes

This method of antenna beam steering offers several advantages over that of mechanically steering the beam by using a servo-driven gimbal system, the most obvious being the capability to steer the antenna at electronic speeds and without mechanical lags. However, the electronic steering technique also causes some nonuniform distortions in the angular spacings among the pattern's lobes, as well as changes in the lobes' amplitudes, compared with those of the unsteered pattern.

In its present state, the voltage pattern model can simulate the boresight pattern of a planar array. It can also handle any variations in sidelobe amplitude through the radial modulation algorithm introduced in Chapter 4. However, in order to simulate the distortions and amplitude effects of beam steering, we must introduce some additional functions. In this chapter, we develop the required directivity functions and apply the model to the simulation of several examples of planar arrays.

6.1 DIRECTIVITY EFFECTS

For this application, we have a computationally simple and functionally accurate modeling technique, which offers an excellent means for simulating the directivity effects of phased arrays. We present the technique by applying the Fourier transform to the development of a basic planar array model, then simplifying the model into a form that is a basic geometric function.

The Fourier model is a stand-alone simulation of a normalized planar array voltage pattern. It does not require any of the previously developed portions of the voltage pattern model for the definition of lobe shapes, boundaries, or amplitudes. However, the Fourier model is somewhat idealized because it presumes a continuous aperture and does not account for amplitude changes resulting from steering. This model is best suited to the application that requires only a planar array model. The Fourier model also requires definition of specific physical and electronic parameters of the array, such as aperture dimensions, frequency of operation, and gain function. The advantage of this model is that it will execute more quickly than the voltage pattern model in most software.

The geometric model is an application of the fundamental concept of the Fourier model to the voltage pattern model developed in the previous chapters. As such, the geometric model is best suited to the application where we know the pattern of an array but do not know the physical and electronic characteristics producing the pattern. It lends itself well to the application where the ability to change easily among several types of antennas is desired, as for a trade-off analysis, for example. The geometric model can be easily fitted to the results of the Fourier model, which offers the capability for efficient optimization of a planar array configuration. The results can then be used as one of several, easily interchangeable antennas in a more diverse application.

6.1.1   The Fourier Model

The model presented here diverges slightly from the normal course of adding capabilities to the antenna voltage pattern model. The Fourier model offers an alternative for planar array simulation, which is less empirical than the voltage pattern model being developed. The derivation serves as a foundation for the geometric model, which is an addition to the voltage pattern model that permits us to simulate beam-steering effects. The electromagnetic theory presented here is not particularly complex, and it allows us to gain an appreciation for the physical interactions involved in electronically steering a planar array.

The foundation of scalar diffraction theory, called *Huygen's principle*, states that any point on a wavefront can be considered an independent source with a spherical wavefront. This principle naturally leads to a surface integration, the far-field solution of which is a Fourier transform.

Examples of this line of thought are common in electromagnetic theory texts. We usually solve these examples for degenerate conditions such as normal illumination with no steering. However, in order to describe the effects of electronic steering with different illumination functions, we need deeper understanding of these effects.

Figure 6.2 shows an example of a circular aperture located on the reference axis system. The aperture lies in the *z-y* plane and is centered at *x* = 0.0.

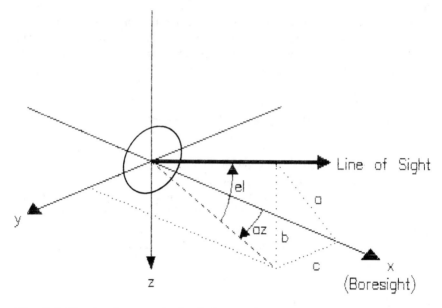

Fig. 6.2 Circular Aperture in the Reference System

If we wish to illuminate this circular aperture and achieve pointing, the illumination must be a plane wave traveling in the direction of pointing. In other words, if we want the maximum amplitude of the pattern to be at some particular azimuth and elevation angles, then the plane wave illuminating the aperture must point to these same azimuth and elevation angles. Figure 6.3 shows a steered illumination pattern on the aperture, showing the lines of zero phase shift, which are separated by a distance of one wavelength along a line in the direction of pointing.

Notice that the intersection of the lines of zero phase shift with the *y* and *z* axes occurs at different points for the steered case than it would for the unsteered case. The distances between these intersections define the relative wavelengths of the illuminating plane wave along the two axes, as Figure 6.3 shows. These relative wavelengths define the progressive phase shift to which we may attribute the steering phenomenon.

As a matter of mathematical convenience for later application, we can describe the relative wavelengths as the ratios of their magnitudes to that of the absolute wavelength:

$$R_y = \lambda/\lambda_y \qquad\qquad\qquad\qquad (6.1)$$
$$R_z = \lambda/\lambda_z$$

where

R_y = wavelength ratio along the y-axis
R_z = wavelength ratio along the z-axis
λ_y = relative wavelength along the y-axis
λ_z = relative wavelength along the z-axis
λ = absolute wavelength in the direction of propagation

The wavelength ratios defined above can be thought of as frequency direction cosines. In vector analysis, a direction cosine is simply the magnitude of the component of the vector along one of the coordinate axes divided by the absolute magnitude of the vector. In this case, if the frequency of the illumination function is considered to be the magnitude of a vector in the direction of steering, then three direction cosines may be defined as

$$a_x = F_x/F$$
$$a_y = F_y/F \qquad\qquad\qquad\qquad (6.2)$$
$$a_z = F_z/F$$

where

F_x, F_y, F_z = frequencies along the three coordinate axes
a_x, a_y, a_z = direction cosines for the three coordinate axes
F = absolute frequency

Frequency, of course, is related to wavelength as an inverse function of the propagation velocity:

$$F = V_c/\lambda \qquad\qquad\qquad\qquad (6.3)$$

where

F = frequency
λ = wavelength
V_c = propagation velocity (speed of light)

We can then define the direction cosines in terms of wavelength instead of frequency by substituting the result of (6.3) into the expressions of (6.2). When we have defined the direction cosines for the y-axis and z-axis, we obtain

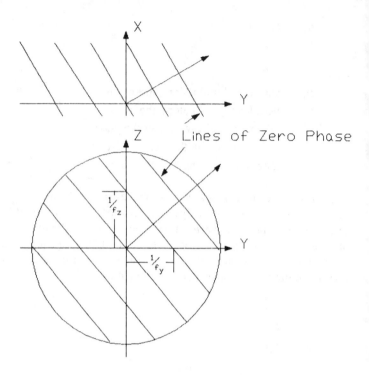

Fig. 6.3 Steered Beam

results that are identical to the wavelength ratios for these two axes, defined by
(6.1):

$$a_y = (V_c/\lambda_y)/(V_c/\lambda) = \lambda/\lambda_y = R_y$$
$$a_z = (V_c/\lambda_z)/(V_c/\lambda) = \lambda/\lambda_z = R_z$$

The reader may conceptually prefer either wavelength ratios or frequency
direction cosines. However, they are mathematically equivalent, and because
wavelength is more conveniently related to phase shift, we will use the wavelength ratio concept here. The relative and absolute wavelengths along the axes
can be related as functions of the steering angles by using simple geometric
transformations. Because the sine of the elevation angle is the wavlength divided
by the relative wavelength along the z-axis, we may redefine the wavelength
ratio as

$$R_z = \lambda/\lambda_z = \sin\theta_{pe} \tag{6.4}$$

where θ_{pe} is the elevation steering angle.

The projection of the absolute wavelength on the x-y plane, or azimuth plane, is simply the absolute wavelength divided by the cosine of the elevation steering angle:

$$\lambda_a = \lambda/\cos\theta_{pe}$$

Then, the sine of the azimuth steering angle is this projected wavelength divided by the relative wavelength along the y-axis. Rearranging terms results in a new expression for the wavelength ratio along the y-axis:

$$(\lambda/\cos\theta_{pe})/\lambda_z = \sin\theta_{pa} \tag{6.5}$$
$$R_y = \lambda/\lambda_z = \sin\theta_{pa}\cos\theta_{pe}$$

where
θ_{pa} = azimuth steering angle
θ_{pe} = elevation steering angle

The utility of (6.4) and (6.5) will become apparent later in this section. At this point, we need only remember that an amplitude illumination function for the aperture, regardless of its form, does not change with steering. Phase steers the array, while the amplitude illumination function remains unchanged and explicitly defines the unsteered pattern.

We may introduce the Fourier transform concepts by examining the field equations for a linear radiator, which is considered to be a current strip of some finite length L. Figure 6.4 illustrates a traditional reference system for the linear radiator, illuminating a point, P, at coordinates (D,R).

If the current through the radiator is continuous and sinusoidal in time, the traditional field pattern derivation gives the field intensity at P as

$$E(D,R) = \int_L \frac{I(x)\exp(-jk\rho)}{\rho}dx$$

where
$E(D,R)$ = electric field intensity
$I(x)$ = current distribution
k = wavenumber $(2\pi/\lambda)$

The conventional approximation for ρ is

$$\rho \approx \rho_0 - \frac{xy}{\rho_0} + \frac{x^2}{2\rho_0}$$

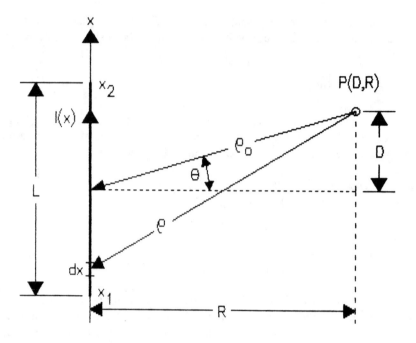

Fig. 6.4 Linear Radiator Geometry

We can then express the complex field strength as

$$E(D,R) = \frac{k \exp(-jk\rho_0)}{\rho_0}$$
$$\int_L I(x)\exp\left[-jk\left(-\sin\theta + \frac{x^2}{2\rho_0}\right)\right]dx$$

Finally, letting $u = \sin\theta$ and isolating the integral portion of the field strength equation results in an expression for relative electric field strength as a function of u:

$$f(u) = \int_L I(x)\exp\left[jk\left(xu - \frac{x^2}{2\rho_0}\right)\right]dx$$

In this expression, the linear term ($jkxu$) is the far-field, or Fraunhofer, zone component. The quadratic term describes the near-field, or Fresnel, zone. We may obtain the far-field solution, which is pertinent to antenna situations, by eliminating the near-field component and evaluating the integral:

$$f(u) = \int_L I(x)\exp(jkxu)dx$$

$$f(u) = \left.\frac{\exp(jkxu)}{jkuL}\right|_{-L/2}^{+L/2}$$

$$f(u) = \frac{\sin(\pi\frac{L}{\lambda}u)}{\pi\frac{L}{\lambda}u}$$

Next, a linear, progressive phase shift can be applied to the radiator by adding an excitation of the form:

$$I_1(x) = I_0(x)\exp(jkax)$$

The expression for the far-field relative electric field strength now reflects the added phase-shifted excitation. We easily recognize the solution as a modified form of the sinc function, previously discussed in Chapter 3:

$$f(u) = \frac{\sin\left[\pi\frac{L}{\lambda}(u-a)\right]}{\pi\frac{L}{\lambda}(u-a)}$$

Because the variable u in this expression represents the sine of the look angle for the linear radiator, the variable a must represent a shifting or steering of the look angle in sine space. Then, the steering angle for the linear radiator, θ_p can be defined as

$$\theta_p = \sin^{-1}(a)$$

This is a significant principle because the same expression can be used for the steered and unsteered linear radiator. The only difference is that when steering is present, the argument of the function is the difference of the sines of the look and steering angles:

$$f(u) = \frac{\sin\left[\pi\frac{L}{\lambda}(\sin\theta - \sin\theta_p)\right]}{\pi\frac{L}{\lambda}(\sin\theta - \sin\theta_p)}$$

In other words, the steered electric field strength is found by transforming the function of the look and steering angles into functions of the sines of these angles, where the steering simply produces a shift with no distortion. This is a Fourier transform for a simple function. Examples of the shifted and unshifted field strength patterns in sine space for a 30° steering angle are shown in Figure 6.5.

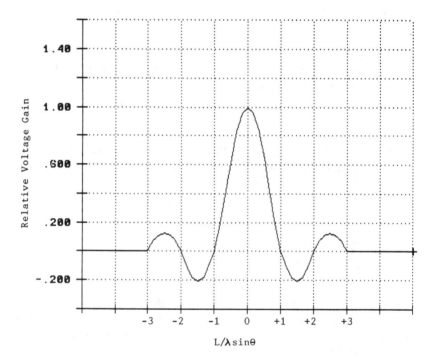

Fig. 6.5(a) Unshifted Pattern in Sine Space

Figure 6.6 illustrates these same electric field strength patterns, plotted as a function of θ. The act of transforming the patterns back into linear space results in the expected angular distortion.

The fundamental principle, then, is that of transforming the electric field strength function into sine space, applying the shift due to steering, and transforming back to linear space. This process is also valid for two-dimensional planar arrays, but the mathematics must be extended to accommodate steering and look angles in both azimuth and elevation.

Mathematically, we can easily extend the linear radiator example into the case of a two-dimensional planar array once we know a certain fact. This fact is that the previously defined variables, *u* and *a*, are actually frequency direction cosines, or wavelength ratios, as described earlier in this section.

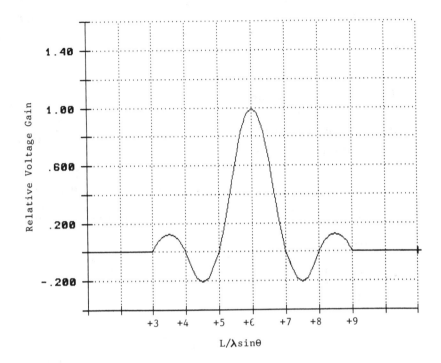

Fig. 6.5(b) Pattern Shifted 30° in Sine Space

Assume that a phased array is pointed to some arbitrary azimuth and elevation angle. The wavelength ratios may be calculated as

$$R_{pz} = \sin\theta_{pe} \tag{6.6}$$

$$R_{py} = \sin\theta_{pa} \cos\theta_{pe} \tag{6.7}$$

where

R_{pz} = z-axis wavelength ratio
R_{py} = y-axis wavelength ratio
θ_{pa} = azimuth pointing angle
θ_{pe} = elevation pointing angle

Next, assume that we desire the gain of the antenna in some direction defined by some azimuth and elevation look angles. The wavelength ratios for the look angles may be calculated as

$$R_{lz} = \sin\theta_{le} \tag{6.8}$$

$$R_{ly} = \sin\theta_{la} \cos\theta_{le} \tag{6.9}$$

where

R_{lz} = z-axis wavelength ratio
R_{ly} = y-axis wavelength ratio
θ_{la} = azimuth look angle
θ_{le} = elevation look angle

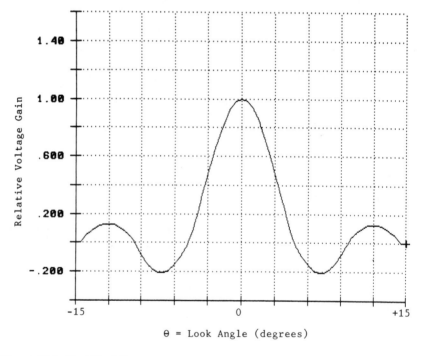

Fig. 6.6(a) Unshifted Pattern

Now that we have transformed the pointing and look angles into sine space, we may calculate their differences to determine the azimuth and elevation wavelength ratios, in sinusoidal space, at which we can interrogate the gain function:

$$R_z = (R_{lz} - R_{pz})$$
$$R_y = (R_{ly} - R_{py})$$

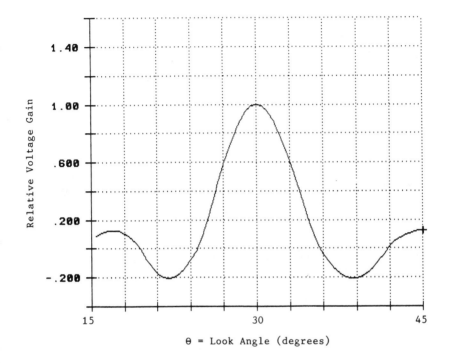

Fig. 6.6(b) Pattern Shifted 30°

The absolute interrogation angle may be found by converting the azimuth and elevation components back to linear space, and calculating the composite angle:

$$\theta = \sin^{-1}\left(R_z^2 + R_y^2\right)^{1/2} \qquad (6.10)$$

where θ is the interrogation angle of the pattern function.

This composite angle is then used as the argument of the pattern function. At this point, the nature of the pattern function is arbitrary. This pattern function may be as simple as the sinc function, or an extremely complex function. The point is that the distortion effects due to pointing were accomplished in the definition of the argument of the function, allowing us to calculate the pattern with no modification to the function itself. A functional flow diagram of the Fourier model appears in Figure 6.7.

As an example of the Fourier model, assume that we want to simulate a planar array with a 0.48-meter diameter aperture and a 7.5 GHz operating frequency. Further, assume that the pattern function to be used is the sinc function:

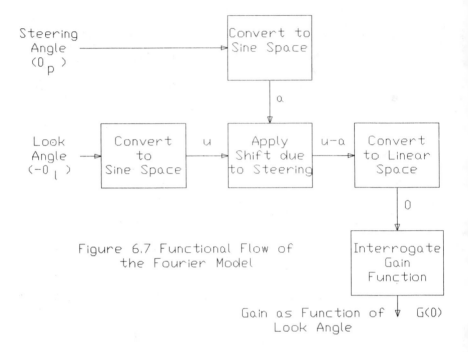

Fig. 6.7 Functional Flow of the Fourier Model

$$G_v = \frac{\sin\left[\pi\frac{D}{\lambda}(\sin\theta)\right]}{\pi\frac{D}{\lambda}(\sin\theta)} \qquad (6.11)$$

Because the aperture diameter and operating frequency are known, the coefficients for (6.11) may be calculated and inserted into the equation:

$$
\begin{aligned}
D &= 0.48 \text{ m} \\
\lambda &= (3 \times 10^8)/(7.5 \times 10^9) = 0.04 \text{ m} \qquad (6.12) \\
D/\lambda &= 0.48/0.04 = 12 \\
G_v &= \frac{\sin[\pi(12)(\sin\theta)]}{\pi(12)(\sin\theta)}
\end{aligned}
$$

For the unsteered case, the resulting three-dimensional voltage pattern is shown in Figure 6.8. This is simply a three-dimensional sinc function.

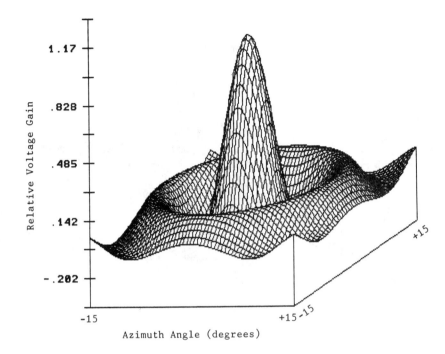

Azimuth Angle (degrees)

Fig. 6.8 Unsteered Voltage Pattern

Next, let us assume that the array is steered to $+35°$ in azimuth and $+25°$ in elevation. The resulting three-dimensional voltage pattern showing the angular distortion is shown in Figure 6.9.

Notice that the distorted pattern of Figure 6.9 is normalized to a value of 1.0 at its peak. As was mentioned before, this simple model does not account for decreasing gain due to pointing, but it does serve to model the angular distortion effects due to steering when we know the pattern of the array. In this example, the sinc function was used for the voltage gain function. However, we could insert a much more complex gain function and experiment with it to obtain a desired pattern under various steering conditions. Once the desired effects were achieved, the pattern could be fitted with the voltage pattern model for actual use in a simulation requiring faster execution time. The next section introduces steering effects into the voltage pattern model.

6.1.2 The Geometric Model

The fundamental concept introduced in the previous section made transformations in and out of sine space. For any steering angle, we obtained the

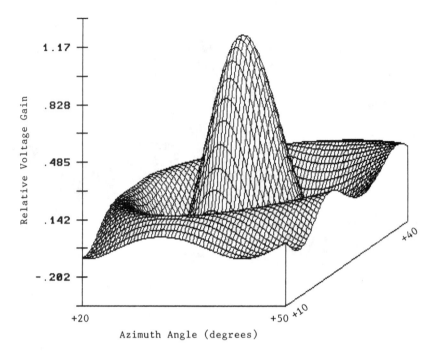

Fig. 6.9 Steered Voltage Pattern

normalized gain of the antenna at any look angle by transforming the steering and look angles into sine space, applying the sinusoidal shift appropriate to the steering angle, then transforming the argument of the gain function back into linear space.

The difficulty in applying this concept is directly related to the nature of the gain function. Some functions are the result of multiple integrations and would have to be implemented as a look-up table rather than a continuous function. Fortunately, the fundamental concept of sine-space transformation may be applied to the voltage pattern model developed in the previous chapters in a very simple and straightforward manner. The sine-space transformation permits us to apply the amplitude and distortion effects of electronic pointing to a model based on the shape of a pattern, rather than on its gain function. The advantage is that we do not have to know or deal with the illumination and gain functions of the antenna being modeled.

The angular distortion effect due to electronically steering a planar array can be handled in a fashion similar to the angular distortion algorithm previously discussed in Section 4.3. Recall that this technique is simply scaling the azimuth and elevation components of the look angle by some constant distortion factor. For the present case of pointing distortion, we use a similar technique, except that for any steering angle, there will be a unique distortion factor for every individual azimuth and elevation component of the look angle rather than simply one constant factor for azimuth and another for elevation.

Consider an unsteered antenna pattern. For simplicity, the elevation component of the look angle is considered to be 0.0 and both look angles and steering angles are considered only in the azimuth plane. Therefore, for any look angle θ, there is some particular normalized gain.

If this pattern is steered to some angle, θ_p, there is a different look angle, θ_s, at which that same particular normalized gain will occur. Therefore, if the equivalent-gain unsteered look angle, θ, can be calculated from the look angle under steering, θ_s, then the pattern model can be interrogated with θ to obtain the proper gain. By convention, the look angle is relative to the boresight of the antenna. Figure 6.10 illustrates the extension of this convention to steering in terms of the angles discussed above.

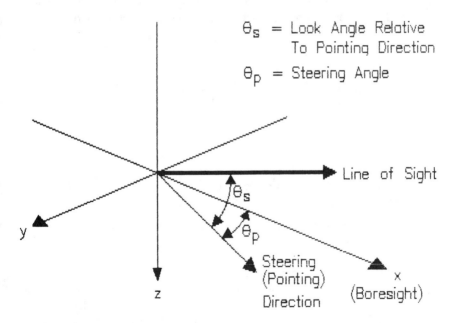

Fig. 6.10 Convention for Relationship between Look Angle and Steering Angle

Figure 6.10 shows that the look angle is always defined relative to the electronic boresight. The physical, or mechanical, boresight is identical to the electronic boresight only when the steering angle θ_p is equal to 0.0.

Now, in linear angular space, the total angle for the steered condition relative to the physical boresight is defined as θ_t and is calculated as

$$\theta_t = \theta_p + \theta_s$$

Recall from the discussions of Section 6.1.1 that no angular distortion exists in sine space. Therefore, the total angle θ_t can be related to the equivalent-gain unsteered look angle θ in sine space as

$$\sin\theta + \sin\theta_p = \sin\theta_t \qquad (6.13)$$
$$\sin\theta + \sin\theta_p = \sin(\theta_p + \theta_s)$$

Solving (6.13) for θ provides a useful expression for the equivalent-gain look angle:

$$\theta = \sin^{-1}\left[\sin(\theta_p + \theta_s) - \sin\theta_p\right]$$

According to the wavelength ratio definitions introduced in the previous section, this concept can be extended to both angular planes as follows:

$$\theta_{ee} = \sin^{-1}[\sin(\theta_{pe} + \theta_{se}) - \sin\theta_{pe}] \qquad (6.14)$$

$$\theta_{ae} = \sin^{-1}\left[\frac{\sin(\theta_{pa} + \theta_{sa})\cos(\theta_{pe} + \theta_{se}) - \sin\theta_{pa}\cos\theta_{pe}}{\cos\theta_{ee}}\right] \qquad (6.15)$$

where

θ_{ae} = equivalent-gain azimuth angle

θ_{ee} = equivalent-gain elevation angle

θ_{pa} = azimuth pointing angle

θ_{pe} = elevation pointing angle

θ_{sa} = azimuth look angle

θ_{se} = elevation look angle

(6.14) and (6.15) accomplish the required angular distortion by calculating equivalent-gain azimuth and elevation look angle components with which to interrogate the voltage pattern model. Functionally within the voltage pattern model, these equations are simply used to modify the look angle components before we perform the voltage pattern calculation, as shown in Figure 6.11.

6.2 STEERING EFFECTS ON PEAK GAIN

The process of electronically pointing a planar array affects the amplitude of the voltage pattern as well as the angular characteristics of the pattern. The

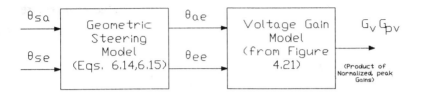

Fig. 6.11 Application of Electronic Steering to the Voltage Gain Model

two factors that influence the pattern's magnitude are changes in effective aperture and beamwidth.

The aperture of a planar array is essentially the area over which the antenna elements are distributed. If we presume a continuous aperture effect, then the power density associated with the array, whether transmitting or receiving, is simply the power divided by the aperture area:

$$P_d = P/A \qquad\qquad (6.16)$$

where

P_d = power density, in W/m^2
P = power, in W
A = aperture area, in m^2

Figure 6.12 illustrates this concept for both a steered and unsteered planar array. In the case of the steered array, it is apparent that the effective aperture in the direction of pointing is reduced by a factor that is the cosine of the steering angle, θ_p:

$$A_e = A \cos\theta_p$$

where A_e is the effective aperture area.

Because the steering angle consists of components in two orthogonal planes (azimuth and elevation), its cosine can be expressed as the product of the cosines of its components. This results in a modified expression for effective aperture:

$$A_e = A(\cos\theta_{pa}\cos\theta_{pe})$$

where

θ_{pa} = azimuth pointing angle
θ_{pe} = elevation pointing angle

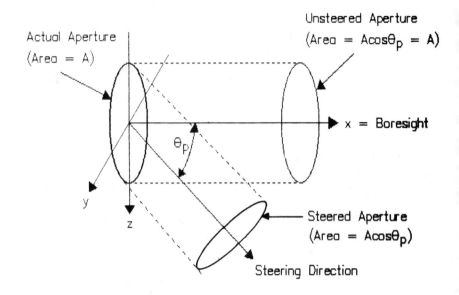

Fig. 6.12 Steering Effect on Effective Aperture Area

Now we can calculate the power transmitted or received under this steering condition. The power is simply the product of the power density from (6.16) and the effective area:

$$P_e = P_d A_e = P[A(\cos\theta_{pa} \cos\theta_{pe})]/A$$
$$= P(\cos\theta_{pa} \cos\theta_{pe})$$

Consequently, we can define a power steering coefficient due to the reduction in effective aperture as

$$C_s = P_e/P = \cos\theta_{pa} \cos\theta_{pe}$$

Therefore, we must multiply any calculated power by this coefficient to account for steering. However, because the model is designed to operate in voltage gain, it is useful to convert the power steering coefficient to this domain:

$$G_{sa} = (\cos\theta_{pa} \cos\theta_{pe})^{1/2} \tag{6.17}$$

where

G_{sa} = voltage gain steering coefficient
θ_{pa} = azimuth pointing (steering) angle
θ_{pe} = elevation pointing (steering) angle

The process of steering the planar array also affects the pattern of the antenna by widening the beamwidth of the main lobe. The actual loss caused by this situation may be calculated as a function of the angular distortion at the half-power beamwidth.

In Chapter 4, we developed an expression for calculating the azimuth and elevation angles at which the relative power gain of the main lobe is equal to half the peak gain. This expression resulted in the calculation of azimuth and elevation beamwidths, which were designated as

$\theta_h D_a / 100$ = azimuth beamwidth, θ_{ha}

$\theta_h D_e / 100$ = elevation beamwidth, θ_{he}

where

θ_h = beamwidth, a function of the voltage pattern model coefficients

D_a = azimuth distortion coefficient, a percentage

D_e = elevation distortion coefficient, a percentage

Notice that the difference between azimuth and elevation is handled by the distortion coefficients. This permits the use of the single beamwidth, θ_h.

Recall that the user could either calculate the peak gain from this beamwidth or insert it directly into the model's off-line process, at the user's discretion. However, even in cases where the peak gain was inserted, the beamwidth calculated from the model coefficients provides a basis for calculating steering effects on peak gain, provided that the model was properly fitted to the pattern being simulated.

The positive and negative azimuth and elevation half-power half-angles may be designated as follows:

$+\theta_{ha}/2$ = positive azimuth half-angle

$-\theta_{ha}/2$ = negative azimuth half-angle

$+\theta_{he}/2$ = positive elevation half-angle

$-\theta_{he}/2$ = negative elevation half-angle

These half-angles, in the unsteered pattern, represent the equivalent gain angles for four half-power half-angles in the steered pattern. The four steered half-power half-angles, θ_{psa}, θ_{nsa}, θ_{pse}, and θ_{nse}, may be calculated by rearranging (6.14) and (6.15) and inserting the unsteered half-power half-angles:

$$\theta_{se} = \sin^{-1}\left(\sin\theta_h + \sin\theta_{pe}\right) - \theta_{pe} \qquad (6.18)$$

$$\theta_{sa} = \sin^{-1}\left[\frac{\sin\theta_h \cos\theta_h + \sin\theta_{pa} \cos\theta_{pe}}{\cos\left(\theta_{pe} + \theta_{se}\right)}\right] - \theta_{pa} \qquad (6.19)$$

Table 6.1 further defines the above equations.

Table 6.1

If θ_h is	then θ_{se} is	and θ_{sa} is
$+\theta_h/2$	θ_{pse}	θ_{psa}
$-\theta_h/2$	θ_{nse}	θ_{nsa}

The loss associated with the angular distortion induced by steering may be calculated as a function of the steered and unsteered half-power angles. Recall from Chapter 4 that the peak power gain is a function of the product of the half-power full-angles or beamwidths:

$$G_{pp} = \frac{4\pi}{\left(\theta_h D_a/100\right)\left(\theta_h D_e/100\right)}$$

where G_{pp} is the unsteered peak power gain.

For the case of a steered array, the half-power full-angles in the expression above are simply the differences between the positive and negative half-power half-angles, which result in a modification to this equation:

$$G_{pps} = \frac{4\pi}{\left(\theta_{psa} - \theta_{nsa}\right)\left(D_a/100\right)\left(\theta_{pse} - \theta_{nse}\right)\left(D_e/100\right)}$$

where G_{pps} is the steered peak power.

Therefore, the peak power gain calculated for the unsteered planar array may be converted to that of the steered array as follows:

$$G_{pps} = G_{pp} \frac{\theta_h^2}{\left(\theta_{psa} - \theta_{nsa}\right)\left(\theta_{pse} - \theta_{nse}\right)}$$

This equation defines a power steering coefficient, due to increased beamwidth, as

$$\frac{G_{pps}}{G_{pp}} = \frac{\theta_h^2}{\left(\theta_{psa} - \theta_{nsa}\right)\left(\theta_{pse} - \theta_{nse}\right)}$$

As with the reduced-aperture steering coefficient, the increased-beamwidth coefficient is converted to operate in the voltage gain domain:

$$G_{sb} = \left(\frac{G_{pps}}{G_{pp}}\right)^{1/2} = \frac{\theta_h}{\left[(\theta_{psa} - \theta_{nsa})(\theta_{pse} - \theta_{nse})\right]^{1/2}} \qquad (6.20)$$

We can finally summarize the voltage gain effects due to steering. If an unsteered planar array is configured to have a normalized voltage gain of G_v and a peak voltage gain of G_{pv}, then the actual voltage gain, considering steering effects, is

$$G_{vs} = G_v G_{pv} G_{sa} G_{sb} \qquad (6.21)$$

where

G_{vs} = combined voltage gain

G_{sa} = aperture reduction coefficient from (6.17)

G_{sb} = beamwidth expansion coefficient from (6.20)

Figure 6.13 illustrates how the aperture reduction and beamwidth expansion effects of steering are incorporated into the model. Notice that we apply the loss term based on the increased half-power beamwidth, even when we insert rather than calculate the peak gain. Because we consider the product of the azimuth and elevation half-power beamwidths an acceptable approximation of the full-power solid angle, it is equally acceptable for us to use these beamwidths as a basis for calculating steering losses.

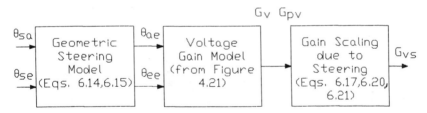

Fig. 6.13 Incorporation of Gain Scaling due to Pointing into the Voltage Gain Model

The following example illustrates how the voltage pattern model may now be used to simulate a steered planar array. Assume that we want the voltage pattern of the example given in Section 6.1.1. Because the gain function of this pattern is known, it may be plotted to facilitate the fitting process, as shown in Figure 6.14.

Using the fitting procedures outlined in Chapter 5, we may determine a set of coefficients for the voltage pattern model. These coefficients and the resulting voltage pattern are shown in Figure 6.15.

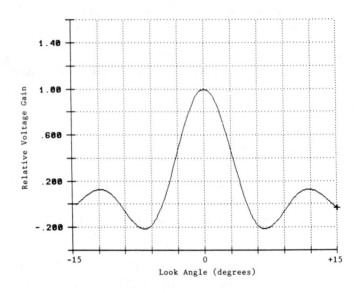

Fig. 6.14 Voltage Pattern to Be Simulated

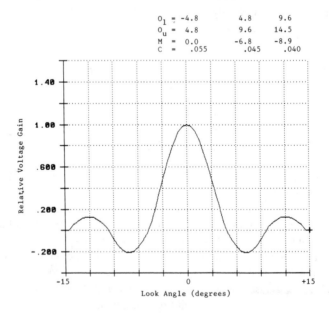

Fig. 6.15 Model-Generated Simulation of Desired Pattern

The three-dimensional voltage pattern for an unsteered condition is illustrated in Figure 6.16. This pattern is a good reproduction of the sinc function of Figure 6.8, to which it was fitted.

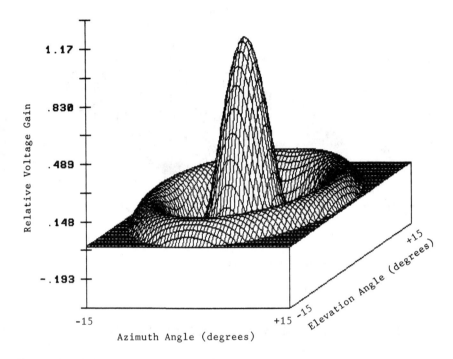

Fig. 6.16 Model-Generated Unsteered Pattern

Figure 6.17 shows this pattern steered to +35° azimuth and +25° elevation. The angular distortion compares to that of Figure 6.9, which illustrated the effect of the same steering angles applied to the sinc function. Additionally, Figure 6.17 shows how the decrease in gain amplitude due to the reduced effective aperture is handled in the voltage pattern model, compared to the ideal case of Figure 6.9.

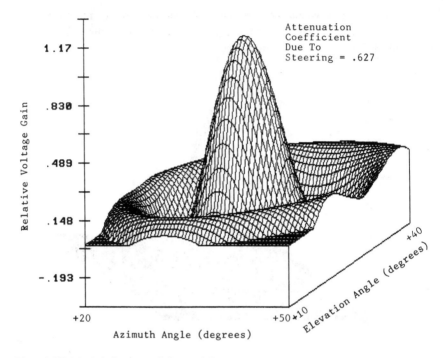

Fig. 6.17 Model-Generated Steered Pattern

6.3 PLANAR ARRAY CROSS-POLARIZED PATTERN

As with other antennas, the planar array exhibits a pattern in the orthogonal polarization. This cross-polarized pattern is generally similar to that of the other antenna types in that Condon-like lobes occur. In the absence of a radome, the planar array cross-polarized gain may be as much as 50–60 dB below that of the co-polarized plane, in which case it can usually be ignored.

However, a radome can have the effect of enhancing the cross-polarized response of the array. This radome effect is not addressed in Part III of this book because its explicit mathematical representation is quite cumbersome. Fortunately, the effect of this phenomenon is simply a redefined pattern consisting of lobes with certain gains, shapes, and angular positions, which may be adequately made by the antenna pattern model.

We may model the radome-enhanced cross-polarized pattern by following the procedures outlined in Chapter 5. As with the horn and reflector antennas, we do not usually find cross-polarized planar array patterns in the open literature for a particular antenna. However, the patterns are generally similar to those of Figure 6.18, although the radial modulation characteristics beyond the first set of lobes may vary considerably as a function of the actual array.

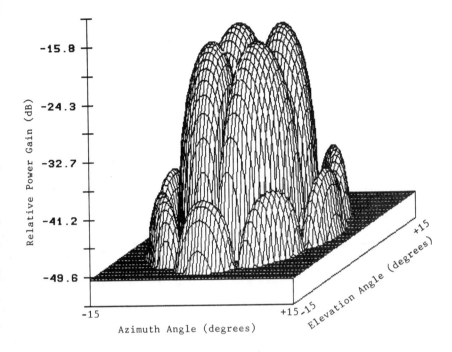

Fig. 6.18 Example of Planar Array Cross-Polarized Pattern

6.4 SUMMARY

This chapter illustrated how the process of planar array steering affects the pattern of the array. We derived a Fourier model from basic electromagnetic theory, and we presented an example of how this model may be used when the pattern function is known.

We then introduced the Fourier technique into the antenna voltage pattern model developed in the previous chapters, thus providing a means for modeling the steering effects of an antenna pattern for which the explicit mathematical function is either unknown or overly complex.

Finally, we discussed the modeling of planar array cross-polarized patterns. We have thereby completed the antenna pattern model. It is capable of modeling virtually any antenna pattern through the definition of its set-up coefficients. In the next, and final, chapter pertaining to antenna modeling, the antenna pattern model is configured into a multiple-antenna tracking system.

Chapter 7
Application to Monopulse Tracking Systems

In radar applications, we may combine several antennas into an antenna system, usually for the purpose of tracking a target. By configuring the antennas in a precise and known geometric relationship, we may use the amplitudes of the radar return signals from the individual antennas for the mathematical determination of the azimuth and elevation angles of a reflective or emissive target.

This chapter shows how the antenna pattern model developed in the previous chapters may be applied to the simulation of a type of multiple-antenna tracking system called a *monopulse system*. This type of tracking system, so named because of its ability to discriminate azimuth or elevation angles based on the information returned from a single transmitted pulse, is the most widely used system in practical application.

7.1 MONOPULSE ANTENNA SYSTEMS

We can explain a monopulse antenna configuration most easily by first considering the problem of tracking a target in one plane only (azimuth, for example), then extending the principle to both planes. Figure 7.1 illustrates the individual voltage patterns for a simple, two-antenna monopulse system, suitable for tracking in one plane. Notice that the antennas are configured such that their boresights are separated by a small angular difference, called the *squint angle*.

The mathematical processing in the receiving mode that permits angle discrimination is shown in Figure 7.2. This process consists of determining the sum (Σ) and difference (Δ) of the voltages from each antenna, dividing the difference by the sum, and then multiplying this quotient by a proportionality constant to determine the angle of the signal source.

If the antenna system is receiving a signal from a single reflecting or emitting source, the voltages produced by each antenna may be expressed as the product of the electromagnetic field strength and the antenna gain:

$$V_A = |\mathbf{E}|\,G_{vA}$$
$$V_B = |\mathbf{E}|\,G_{vB}$$

where

V_A = voltage amplitude from antenna A

V_B = voltage amplitude from antenna B

G_{vA} = voltage gain of antenna A

G_{vB} = voltage gain of antenna B

$|\mathbf{E}|$ = magnitude of the electric field intensity from the source

The sum (Σ) and difference (Δ) may be expressed as

$$\Sigma = |\mathbf{E}|\,G_{vA} + |\mathbf{E}|\,G_{vB} = |\mathbf{E}|\,(G_{vA} + G_{vB})$$
$$\Delta = |\mathbf{E}|\,G_{vA} - |\mathbf{E}|\,G_{vB} = |\mathbf{E}|\,(G_{vA} - G_{vB})$$

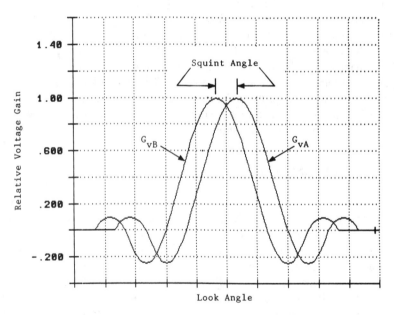

Fig. 7.1 Two Squinted Voltage Patterns

The results of the sum and difference calculations are illustrated in Figure 7.3. We usually choose the squint angle such that the sum pattern does not produce a "dip" at its peak value, which can occur when we select too large a squint angle. Also, we wish to maximize the slope of the difference pattern. These constraints generally result in the selection of a squint angle such that the

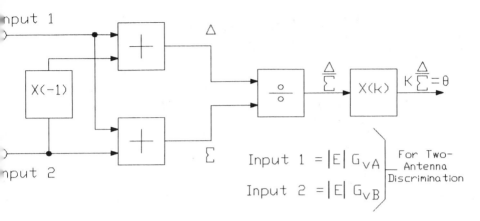

Fig. 7.2 Two-Antenna Monopulse Angle Discrimination Processing

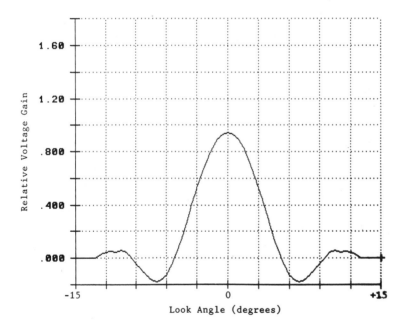

Fig. 7.3(a) Monopulse sum (Σ) Voltage Pattern

power gains for the two individual antennas are about -2 dB at the crossover point.

Taking the quotient of the difference and sum quantities results in two desirable effects. First, the magnitude of the electromagnetic field strength is mathematically canceled:

$$\frac{\Delta}{\Sigma} = \frac{|\mathbf{E}|(G_{vA} - G_{vB})}{|\mathbf{E}|(G_{vA} + G_{vB})} = \frac{G_{vA} - G_{vB}}{G_{vA} + G_{vB}}$$

This expression is effectively an automatic gain control function, which makes the quotient independent of signal strength within the dynamic range of a radar signal processor. The second desirable effect is linearization, as illustrated in Figure 7.4, which shows the result of the difference/sum calculation.

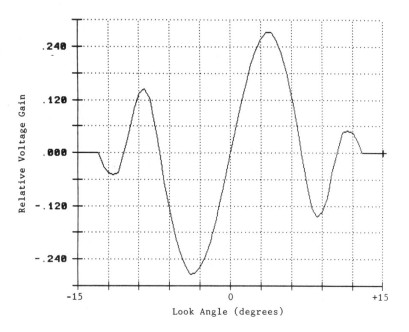

Fig. 7.3(b) Monopulse Difference (Δ) Voltage Pattern

Notice that the function is quite linear through about 70% of the sum pattern's beamwidth. Within this linear tracking range, the angle of the signal source, θ, may be expressed as a linear function of the difference/sum quotient:

$$\theta = K\frac{\Delta}{\Sigma}$$

where K is the reciprocal of the slope of the Δ/Σ function of Figure 7.4.

We may easily extend the principle of angle discrimination described above to two-axis angle tracking. We do so by adding two additional antennas to the system as illustrated in Figure 7.5. This type of configuration is often called a four-horn monopulse. However, because the antennas in the system may be

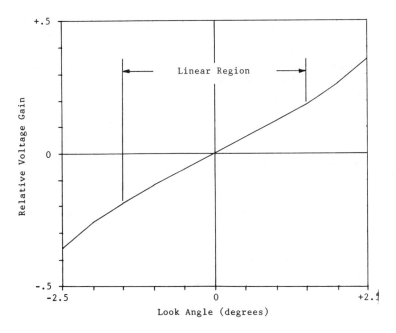

Fig. 7.4 Monopulse Differenc/Sum (Δ/Σ) Function

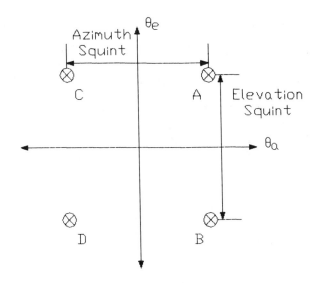

Fig. 7.5 Angular Boresights of Antennas in a Four-Antenna Monopulse Configuration

planar array elements as well as horns, it is more correctly referred to as a *four-antenna monopulse configuration.*

The mathematical process required to extract the azimuth and elevation angles is simply an extension of the two-antenna monopulse process previously shown in Figure 7.2. The four-antenna process, illustrated in Figure 7.6, simply requires some preprocessing to combine the four antenna voltages into an azimuth or elevation configuration.

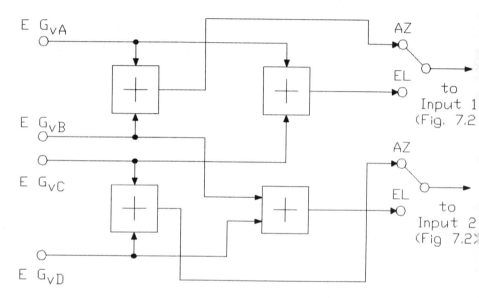

Fig. 7.6 Four-Antenna Monopulse Angle Discrimination Preprocessing

It is important to note that because the four antennas may have different beamwidths in azimuth and elevation, and the azimuth and elevation squint angles may differ, the slopes of the difference/sum function may differ for the two angular axes. The azimuth and elevation tracking functions for the four-antenna monopulse system may be expressed as

$$\theta_a = K_a \left[\frac{(G_{vA} + G_{vB}) - (G_{vC} + G_{vD})}{(G_{vA} + G_{vB} + G_{vC} + G_{vD})} \right] \tag{7.1}$$

$$\theta_e = K_e \left[\frac{(G_{vA} + G_{vC}) - (G_{vB} + G_{vD})}{(G_{vA} + G_{vB} + G_{vC} + G_{vD})} \right] \tag{7.2}$$

where

K_a = azimuth tracking coefficient

K_e = elevation tracking coefficient

The task of implementing the four-antenna monopulse system in a simulation is fairly straightforward. The mathematical process of Figure 7.6 becomes part of the signal processing function, and it may be structured to handle phasor quantities or simple amplitudes as required. From the perspective of the antenna simulation, the only difference now is that we must calculate four individual antenna gains instead of one. Each individual voltage pattern model is structured as described in the previous chapters, and consists of co-polarized and cross-polarized patterns.

In actual simulation, we need not have four individual pattern models. Because the four antennas in a system are identical, we may use a single model with a set of coefficients for co-polarized and cross-polarized patterns. This model is then exercised for four composite look angles, which may be calculated as a function of the look angle of a source with respect to the antenna system boresight and the azimuth and elevation squint angles, as follows:

$$\theta_{e_x} = \left| \theta_e - \theta_{se_x} \right| \tag{7.3}$$

$$\theta_{a_x} = \left| \theta_a - \theta_{sa_x} \right| \tag{7.4}$$

where

x = $A, B, C,$ or D for each of the four antennas in the monopulse system

θ_{a_x} = azimuth angle with respect to the particular antenna

θ_{e_x} = elevation angle with respect to the particular antenna

θ_a = azimuth angle with respect to the antenna system boresight

θ_e = elevation angle with respect to the antenna system boresight

θ_{sa_x} = azimuth squint half-angle

θ_{se_x} = elevation squint half-angle

The relationships among the components of (7.3) and (7.4) are illustrated in Figure 7.7. The outputs of the voltage pattern model, driven by the four look angles, are the four resulting voltage gains from the individual antennas in the monopulse configuration.

The process of determining the coefficients of the co-polarized and cross-polarized pattern model to be used in a four-antenna monopulse configuration

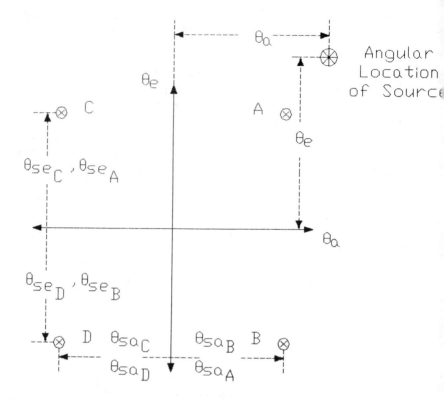

Fig. 7.7 Angular Relationships in a Four-Antenna Monopulsé Configuration

is not exactly straightforward. For example, we often obtain data for the composite sum and difference antenna pattern, rather than that for the individual antennas. Also, we need to consider some subtle differences between horn, reflector, and phased array configurations, as well as interactions with the radome.

We can manage all these aspects, but we often require some iterative analysis, which is somewhat peculiar to the type of antennas in the configuration. The following sections address these peculiarities and demonstrate the process of coefficient determination for these monopulse systems.

7.2 FOUR-HORN MONOPULSE SIMULATION

This section describes the method for determining the voltage pattern model's coefficients for a four-horn monopulse configuration. In this section, the term "four-horn" actually applies to any monopulse configuration except a planar array system. This definition, of course, would include reflector antennas as well as horn antennas.

In order to determine these coefficients, it is useful to configure a test simulation in which coefficients may be tested and changed easily and quickly, in an iterative fashion. Such a simulation appears in Figure 7.8. This system allows the user to select a range of system look angles over which the coefficients are to be tested. The user mathematically transforms the system look angles into the individual look angles for each antenna, and calculates voltage gains as a function of the desired coefficients. These voltage gains for the individual antennas are then used to calculate the sum, difference, and difference/sum quantities, which are stored as files and then converted to displays by the graphics utility. Based on the displayed data, the user may choose to adjust the value of one or more coefficients and repeat the process until he or she obtains satisfactory antenna patterns.

In performing this iterative process, the user will be adjusting individual antenna coefficients, but observing composite system effects. To do this adjustment as efficiently as possible, the user should have an appreciation of how the individual coefficients affect the sum and difference functions.

Typically, the known parameters of a monopulse system are the co-polarized sum and difference patterns. The sum pattern may be used to ascertain several characteristics of the individual horns. Figure 7.9 illustrates typical normalized azimuth sum and difference patterns for a four-horn monopulse.

In a typical monopulse configuration, the squint angle is small compared with the angular widths of the lobes, over the first several sidelobes. Because this is so, we may assume that the slopes of the individual horn patterns are approximately equal between their zero-crossing points, as Figure 7.10 illustrates.

Based on this assumption, the zero crossings of the sum pattern must fall approximately halfway between the zero crossings of the individual patterns, according to the following expression:

$$\theta_\Sigma = \frac{(\theta_A + \theta_S) + (\theta_B - \theta_S)}{2}$$

$$\theta_\Sigma = \frac{\theta_A + \theta_B}{2}$$

and because $\theta_A = \theta_B$,

$$\theta_\Sigma = \theta_A = \theta_B$$

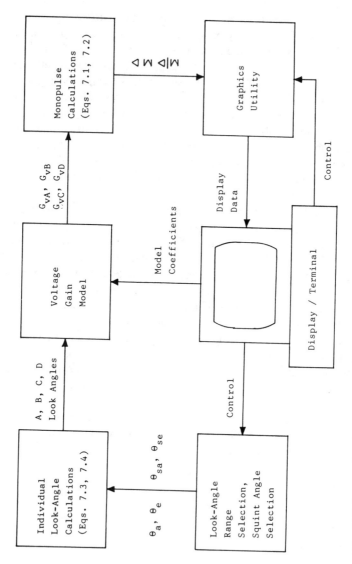

Fig. 7.8 Interactive System for Coefficient Determination

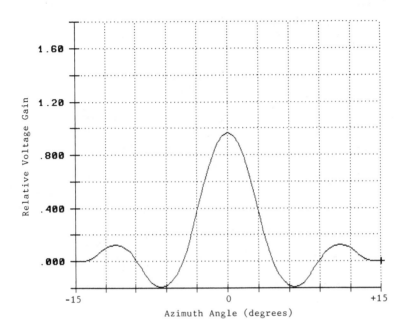

Fig. 7.9(a) Four-Horn Monopulse Azimuth Sum Pattern

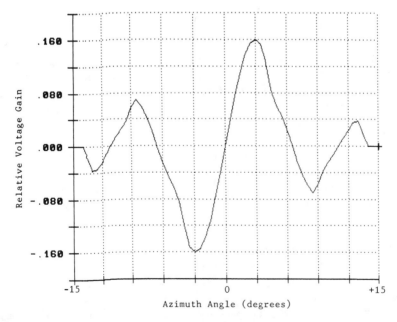

Fig. 7.9(b) Four-Horn Monopulse Azimuth Difference Pattern

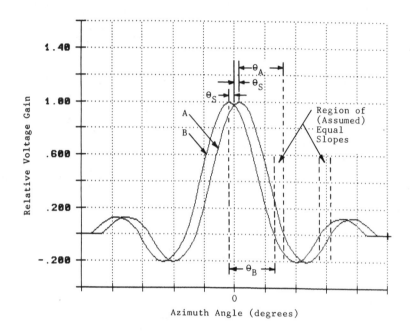

Fig. 7.10 Two Squinted Patterns Showing Slope Assumption

This expression is a reasonable approximation for the zero crossings of the first several sidelobes and establishes the fact that the zero crossings of the sum pattern are a good starting approximation for the angular lobe boundaries of the individual horns. Because the squint angle is quite small compared with the lobe widths, the maximum gains and shapes of the lobes of the sum pattern are also good starting approximations for those of the individual horns. Therefore, the first step in determining the horn coefficients is simply to fit the voltage pattern model to the sum pattern.

In performing this fitting, it is important to notice whether the sum pattern is normalized to its own maximum. If it is, the sum pattern's maximum value will be unity for decimal gain or 0.0 dB for gain expressed in decibels. This being the case, the voltage pattern model may be fitted directly to it, as described in Chapter 5 for an individual horn. However, if the sum power pattern has a peak decimal value of about 4.0 or a decibel value of about 6 dB, then the pattern should be normalized to its maximum value before the fitting process.

Once we have determined the coefficients for the voltage pattern model, we may use them to produce a sum pattern that may be compared to the desired pattern. In doing this, a squint angle must be specified. We can usually obtain a specific value, but if not, we can start with the reasonable assumption that the squint angle is about 1°. The sum pattern produced by these starting assumptions will typically have zero crossings that are close to those desired, and lobe shapes that are somewhat more rounded or wider than desired. Figure 7.11 shows the result of this approach to fitting the sum pattern of Figure 7.9.

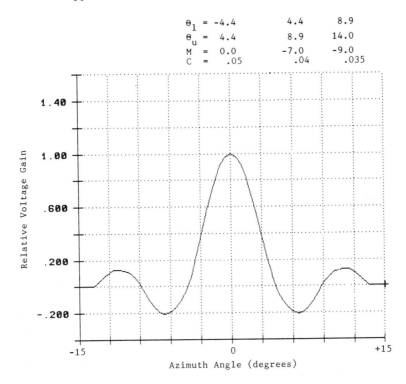

Fig. 7.11 Single-Horn Fit to Sum Pattern of Figure 7.9(a)

    At this point, the iterative analysis begins. Generally, the procedure adjusts the lobe boundaries to achieve the desired zero crossings for the sum pattern, then increases the exponential and triangular shaping coefficients to produce the desired shape. Because adjustments to the shape will affect the zero-crossing angles of the sum pattern, a few iterations of this procedure will usually result in the desired pattern.

    The use of this procedure with the example started in Figure 7.11 ultimately produces the sum pattern of Figure 7.12, with the lobe coefficients listed. Notice that both the boundaries and shaping coefficients of the lobes are slightly altered from those of Figure 7.11 to achieve a proper sum pattern.

    The difference pattern and difference/sum pattern produced by the coefficients determined in this example are shown in Figure 7.13. The reciprocal of the slopes of the azimuth and elevation difference/sum patterns would be the

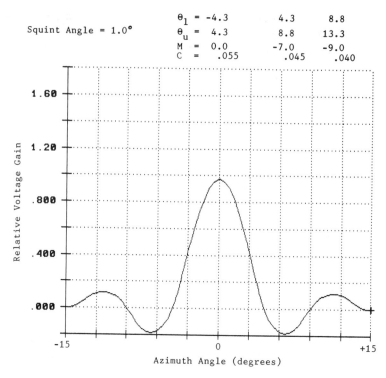

θ_l =	-4.3	4.3	8.8
θ_u =	4.3	8.8	13.3
M =	0.0	-7.0	-9.0
C =	.055	.045	.040

Squint Angle = 1.0°

Fig. 7.12 Model-Generated Fit to Sum Pattern of Figure 7.9(a)

proportionality constants to be used for azimuth and elevation angle discrimination in the signal processing portion of the radar system.

From the discussions just presented, we deduce that the modeling procedure will achieve a fit to the sum pattern, after which the difference pattern follows. This deduction is generally true, but there are some exceptions. Three interdependent quantities are involved here:

• Squint angle;
• Sum pattern shape (or beamwidth);
• Difference/sum pattern slope (error function).

Definition of any two of these quantities will explicitly define the third. In the example just presented, we defined the sum pattern lobe shape and the squint angles and obtained the error function slope from properly fitting the sum pattern. However, the sum pattern shape and the slope of the difference/sum function are the characteristics that determine how well a radar simulation tracks a source. Therefore, these two parameters should be given precedence in cases where all three characteristics may be defined. In other words, if it is necessary to deviate from the given squint angle to satisfy the other two characteristics, then we should do so.

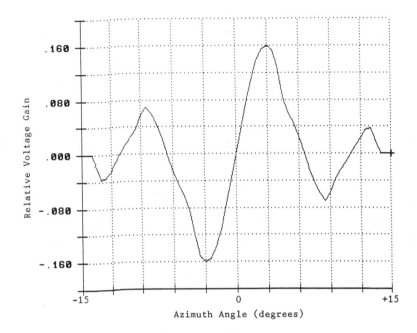

Fig. 7.13(a) Model-Generated Fit to Difference Pattern of Figure 7.9(b)

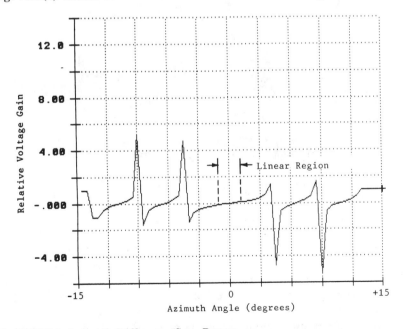

Fig. 7.13(b) Azimuth Difference/Sum Pattern

Because the tracking characteristics of a monopulse antenna system are a function of the shape of the main lobes of the individual horns, it is appropriate to achieve as good a fit as possible. However, in the case of the sidelobes, the level of accuracy required is generally not as critical. For most simulation applications, a good fit to the sidelobe amplitudes and angular boundaries is sufficient, so we need not expend a great deal of effort in obtaining a precise fit to the shapes.

The same procedures outlined above may be used to achieve a fit to the cross-polarized pattern of a four-horn monopulse system. As in the case for the cross-polarized pattern of an individual antenna, it is usually more difficult to obtain the data than it is to fit the model to the data. The cross-polarized patterns of a typical four-horn monopulse system are shown in Figure 7.14, with the individual horn coefficients used to produce them. The cyclic, zero-crossing characteristic of the radial modulation function results in an interesting composite gain characteristic, which is quite different from that of the co-polarized case.

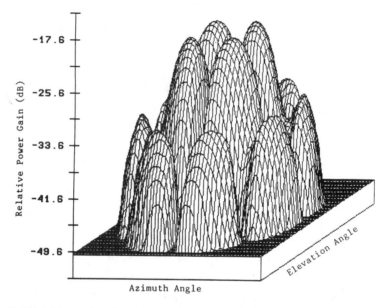

Fig. 7.14(a) Example of a Cross-Polarized Monopulse Sum Pattern

The final issue to discuss for four-horn monopulse modeling is that of radome effects. In certain cases, the electromagnetic interaction between the radome and the horns may produce different distortion effects for the sum and difference patterns. The radome model discussed in Part II of this book can handle radome transmission and refraction effects, but not the distortion. This distortion manifests itself during the fitting process by creating a situation in

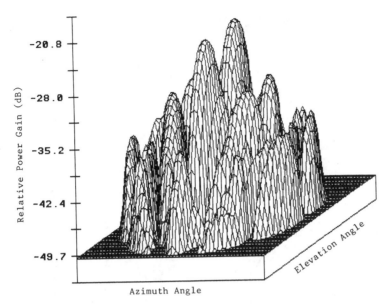

Fig. 7.14(b) Example of a Cross-Polarized Monopulse Azimuth Difference Pattern

which the sum and difference patterns cannot be achieved with a single set of coefficients for the individual horns.

If the distortion effect is minor, we can compromise by configuring a set of coefficients that yields an acceptable level of error for both patterns and, subsequently, has acceptable tracking characteristics. However, if the distortion effect is significant, we may need to use one set of coefficients for the individual horn gain model for the sum pattern, and a different set for the difference pattern. This is an acceptable solution, which merely requires some additional book-keeping within the simulation structure to assign the proper coefficients to the proper functions, as shown in Figure 7.15.

7.3 PLANAR ARRAY MONOPULSE SIMULATION

The use of a planar array in a four-antenna monopulse configuration is based on the same principles discussed previously for the general case and the four-horn system. However, the physical and electronic implementation of an array is significantly different from that of a four-horn system. In a planar array monopulse system, the array is not divided into four discrete physical sections for the four individual antennas. Rather, the elements representing each of the four monopulse components are distributed more or less equally over the array

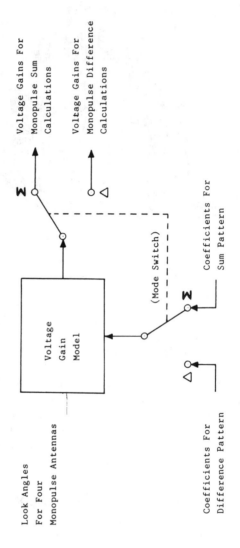

Fig. 7.15 Use of Separate Sets of Coefficients for Sum And Difference

aperture and electronically steered to achieve the squint angle. Further, the sum and difference functions may be obtained directly from the array through waveguide comparators rather than in the signal processing.

Obviously, a rigorous simulation of this configuration would involve a great deal of electromagnetic theory and wavefront geometry. Fortunately, we can simulate this configuration more easily if we do it in precisely the same way as for the four-horn monopulse system, and accept the fact that a different set of coefficients will be required for the voltage pattern model for the sum and difference functions. The following example illustrates this technique.

Assume we wish to simulate the monopulse patterns of Figure 7.16. These represent the sum and azimuth difference relative power patterns for a planar array. Obviously, we would also need to model the elevation difference pattern for an actual simulation, but for simplicity's sake this example will be limited to the azimuth case.

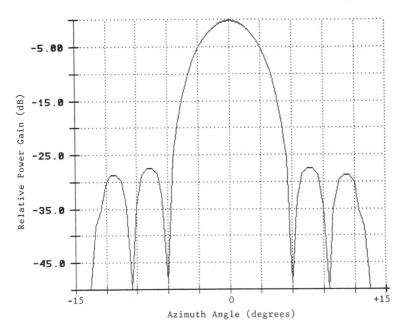

Fig. 7.16(a) Monopulse Sum Pattern to Be Modeled

By applying the modeling techniques given in Section 7.2 to the sum pattern, we may obtain a reasonable fit to the desired pattern. The result of this process is shown as the sum pattern of Figure 7.17 along with the pattern model coefficients that produced this pattern. Although these coefficients produced an

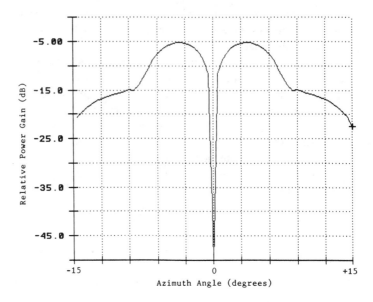

Fig. 7.16(b) Monopulse Difference Pattern to Be Modeled

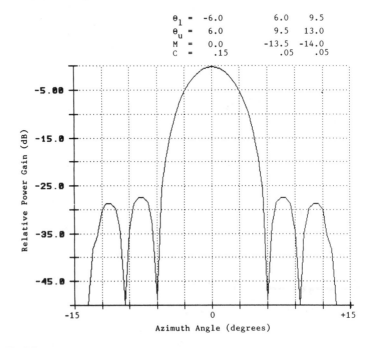

Fig. 7.17(a) Model-Generated Sum Pattern

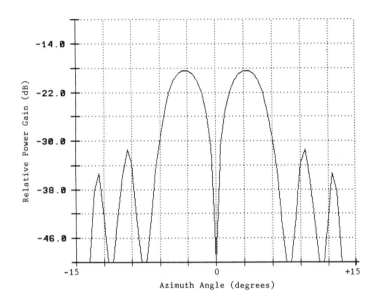

Fig. 7.17(b) Model-Generated Difference Pattern (Same Coefficients)

acceptable simulation of the desired sum pattern, the difference pattern resulting from them bears little resemblance to the desired difference pattern.

Some experimentation with the pattern model coefficients results in the difference pattern of Figure 7.18, which is an acceptable fit to the desired pattern. Because we used different coefficients for the sum and difference patterns, we are able to handle any distortions due to radome-antenna interaction.

The method for modeling the cross-polarized sum and difference patterns for the planar array monopulse system is similar to that for the four-horn monopulse, so we will give no specific examples here. Generally, the planar array cross-polarized pattern will be considerably lower in amplitude than that of the horn or reflector configuration, all other factors being equal. The addition of the radome, however, usually has the effect of increasing the cross-polarized gain relative to the co-polarized gain.

7.4 SUMMARY

This chapter presented methods for incorporating the antenna pattern model, developed in the previous chapters, into a simulation of antenna systems for monopulse tracking radars. The antenna pattern model proved versatile enough to handle both co-polarized and cross-polarized patterns for several types of

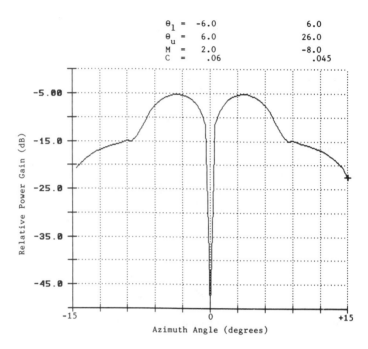

Fig. 7.18 Model-Generated Difference Pattern (New Coefficients)

monopulse antenna systems, including horn, reflector, and planar array configurations. In order to accommodate distortions due to certain radome effects and
the complexities of integrated array configurations, we found it necessary to use
different pattern model coefficients for the purpose of sum and difference pattern
computations. However, the fundamental structure of the pattern model remained
intact, and the process of using different sets of coefficients turned out to be
significantly less complicated and less time-consuming than a more rigorous
simulation technique.

In configuring the voltage pattern model coefficients to achieve the desired
sum and difference patterns in the presence of radome-induced distortion, we
often require considerable latitude in selecting the maximum gains for the lobes.
In some cases, we may need a positive dB voltage gain value. Although this
value may seem intuitively strange, it is perfectly acceptable mathematically and
will cause no problems in the model. Remember that this technique is empirical,
and one of the advantages of such a method is that physical reality can sometimes
be transcended in the interest of ultimate performance.

PART III
RADOMES

The radome simulation model developed in this part of the book is organized somewhat differently than the previously described antenna simulation. The radome transmission function is derived in two parts. In the first part, we will use geometric principles to decompose the electric field into components parallel and perpendicular to the plane of incidence. In the second part, we will use a transmission line analogy to describe the propagation of these components through the radome. The simulation code, presented with the text, offers a useful means for describing the simulation technique. For convenience of future reference, we compiled the program listings in Appendix B, along with their supporting utility routines.

Chapter 8
Geometric Principles

A radome is a lens in every sense of the word. In some systems, the radome can be treated as a scalar loss; in others, it may be the system's limiting element. The transmission of the radome is, of course, the parameter of interest, and it is a function of the radome's construction. But the transmission is also very heavily influenced by the relative positions of the antenna within the radome and the radar target. Because these geometric considerations are so crucial to radome-antenna analysis, it is appropriate to devote a chapter to discussing them.

We will use a single-ray tracing method to analyze the distortions that the radome imparts on the signals passing through it. Many methods are presented in the literature for modeling radome-antenna systems. Depending on the particular effects in which we are interested, these techniques range from full integrations over the radome surface to plane-wave analyses. The single-ray tracing method will accurately describe radome gain (loss) and depolarizing effects. However, the method will account for neither radome-induced sidelobes nor the guiding of radar energy along the radome surface. The model presented here is an approximation, but it represents a good balance between accuracy and computational power and can be used in a dynamic simulation.

Simulations typically quantify the field in terms of an electric field or E-vector, a phasor quantity. Therefore, we are confronted with the specific problem of separating the E-vector into components normal and parallel to the plane of incidence, then calculating the transmission and phase shift for these components. This chapter specifies the shape and geometry of the radome, and determines the components of the E-vector at the intersection point of the radome surface and the line of sight to the target. The subsequent chapters will deal with solving the radome as a function of its layer composition and applying the techniques to specific types of radomes.

The radome algorithm follows a simple and logical sequence to arrive at transmission. First, we use the point at which the look vector from the radar antenna to the target passes through the radome, and the equation for the radome's surface to find the normal, or perpendicular, vector at that point. The angle between the look vector and the normal vector to the radome surface is the angle of incidence, which is determined by taking the dot product of these two vectors. This means that the radome will be considered locally planar at the point of intersection. The look vector and the normal vector also uniquely determine the unit vectors parallel and perpendicular to the surface at the point of intersection. The incident E-vector is decomposed into its parallel and perpendicular components, and these components are scaled by the transmission coefficients. The transmitted parallel and perpendicular components are then reassembled into the total transmitted wave.

The subsequent chapters complete the calculation of transmission and extend the basic concept to actual radome cases. In these cases, the polarization of the signal is determined by the relative orientations of the target and radar antenna, as well as by the characteristic of the signal—for example, whether it is transmitted or reflected, and, if reflected, the nature of the reflecting medium. This polarization, combined with the path lengths and angles through the media of the radome, ultimately determines the magnitude of the normal and tangential electric field components.

8.1 RADOME SHAPE FUNCTION

Although the geometric considerations involved in the shape of a radome can be quite complex, we can make several simplifications to reduce computation time, without greatly decreasing the accuracy of the results. The general, two-dimensional shape of an airborne radome is generally similar to that of Figure 8.1. In this case, the shape is pointed and streamlined for aerodynamic reasons. Conversely, a ground-based radome would be more dome-shaped than streamlined in order to maintain a fairly constant angle of incidence between the look vector and the normal to the radome surface regardless of the direction in which the enclosed radar antenna is pointed. Although actual radomes are not necessarily symmetrical as Figure 8.1 depicts, they may be considered as such for modeling simplicity. The advantages of this simplification will soon become apparent.

We do not present the shape function here because it is the best function to use. Rather, it is only an example of an orderly method to calculate the intersection point with a common and representative radome shape. The radome shape algorithm about to be developed allows us to transform the shape from a dome to a streamlined, pointed shape, or ogive, through a single shaping coefficient. The algorithm is first developed as a two-dimensional function for simplicity's sake, then extended to the required three-dimensional case. The radome shape is defined in terms of a local three-axis coordinate system as shown in

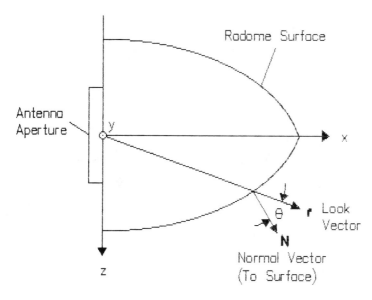

Fig. 8.1 Two-Dimensional $(x-z)$ Radome Shape

Figure 8.2, with its origin located at the center of the aperture of the antenna housed by the radome.

The point of interest is the intersection of the surface with a ray, **r**, representing the line of sight, or look vector, to a target or from a source. The surface may be described in the $x-y$ plane as

$$x = C - y^2$$
$$x + y^2 = C$$
(8.1)

where C is the shaping coefficient. The angle θ between **r** and an outward vector normal to the slope of a plane tangent to the surface at its intersection with **r** is the variable that we must determine first.

This simple parabolic function provides an excellent fit to any ogive-shaped radome. We can control the slope of the surface by adjusting the value of C, which controls the degree of pointedness. The value of C does not necessarily reflect the actual, physical distance from the antenna to the radome point. Because the distance from the antenna to the radome wall is normally quite inconsequential compared to the range from the antenna to the target or source, the units of x, y, and z are arbitrary, and C is simply a dimensionless shaping coefficient. This means that we neglect near-field components for transmission. For reception, the radome is always in the far field.

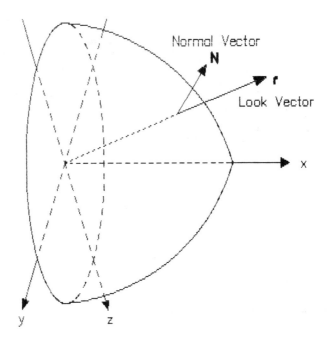

Fig. 8.2 Three-Dimensional $(x - y - z)$ Radome Shape

Figure 8.3 shows how changing the value of C affects the radome shape. This also reveals a limitation in the use of the function, for pointed shapes. As x approaches C, the function tends to round off. This algorithm employs a single-point ray-tracing technique. Therefore, the rounding effect, shown as a dashed line in Figure 8.3, is not acceptable because it would result in a very small incidence angle at the point of the radome, which changes very rapidly as we move only a few degrees from boresight.

We eliminate the rounding effect by creating a mathematical "deadband" for any values of x within 1.0 (arbitrary units) of C. Thus, for any value of x in this band, the slope of the radome surface is limited to a value of $x = C - 1$. This results in a constant slope and constant shape, converging to a point at a value of x slightly larger than C.

As previously mentioned, one of the simplifications employed by this algorithm is the use of a single point of intersection. The difference between a total aperture approach and the single-point approach is depicted in Figure 8.4. If we considered the surface area of the radome subtended by the projection of the antenna aperture along **r**, the surface would have to be broken down into many facets. For each facet, we would have to perform geometric and transmission calculations and determine their overall effect. This is the foundation for surface integration techniques.

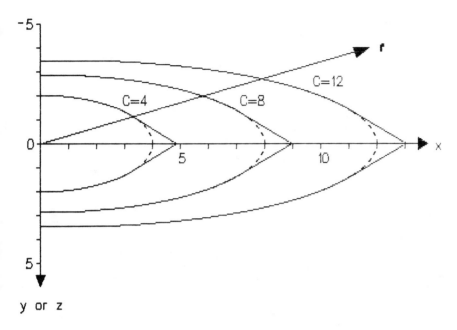

Fig. 8.3 Radome Shape Variations

The single-ray approach provides a significant reduction in computational complexity with no appreciable reduction in accuracy. Because the slope of the surface changes very little across any aperture-subtended segment, the point of intersection of the slope with the ray, **r**, represents a reasonable average effect for the surface. This is true even across the point of the radome, as Figure 8.5 illustrates. As previously discussed, the upper half of the radome surface is identical to the lower half, and the algorithm is prevented from becoming rounded. Therefore, the slope calculated at $C - 1$ represents a good average slope for a ray at or near the x-axis. Although the mathematical slope reverses at the x-axis, the absolute angle of the ray with respect to the surface slope, α, remains constant as **r** crosses the x-axis.

Up to this point, we have discussed the two-dimensional surface shaping function. But the problem is actually three-dimensional, so we must extend the situation to define the surface in three-dimensional space. The electric field vector traveling along **r** must then be separated into components tangential to the surface (a tangential plane being a three-dimensional extension of the slope at a point) and normal to this tangential plane.

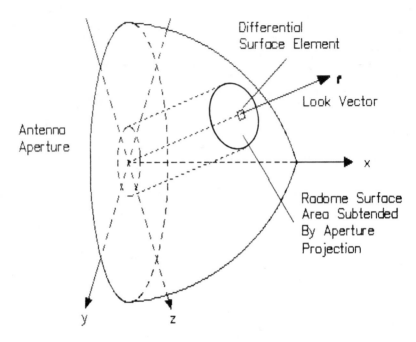

Fig. 8.4 Single Point of Intersection *versus* Aperture Projection

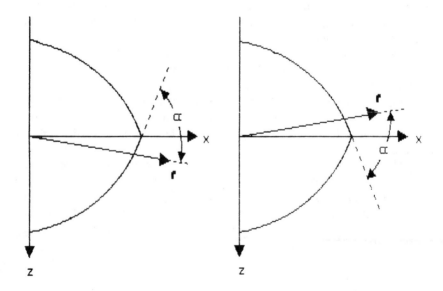

Fig. 8.5 Surface Slope at the Radome Point

8.2   CALCULATION OF THE POINT OF INTERSECTION

The point of intersection for the three-dimensional case will be solved as two separate, two-dimensional problems. Figure 8.6 shows an illustration of the radome and its intersection with the look vector at point (Y_2', X'). The first problem is to solve for X'. Because of the circular symmetry of the radome in the $Y - Z$ plane, X' will be constant for a given θ. Therefore, we need to "rotate" the local coordinate system into Y_2 so that the look vector lies in the $X - Y_2$ plane.

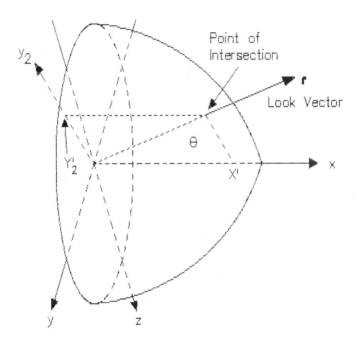

Fig. 8.6 Rotation into the Incidence $(x - y_2)$ Plane

In two dimensions, the equation for the surface of the radome is

$$X + Y_2^2 = C$$

In order to solve for X', we substitute $X' \tan(\theta)$ for Y_2', giving the quadratic in X':

$$\tan^2(\theta) X'^2 + X' - C = 0$$

The correct root to take is the one obtained by using $+(b^2-4ac)^{1/2}$ in the quadratic equation. The length of the ray from the origin to the radome, R, is easily solved as

$$R = X' / \cos(\theta)$$

The values Y' and Z' are simply the unit look vector's Y and Z components multiplied by R.

$$Y' = R \mid \mathbf{y}_l \mid$$
$$Z' = R \mid \mathbf{z}_l \mid$$

where $\mathbf{y}_l$ and $\mathbf{z}_l$ are look vector components. The above operation is simply the unit look vector's Y and Z components times the magnitude of the vector to the radome surface. This solution to the pair of two-dimensional problems is illustrated in Figure 8.7.

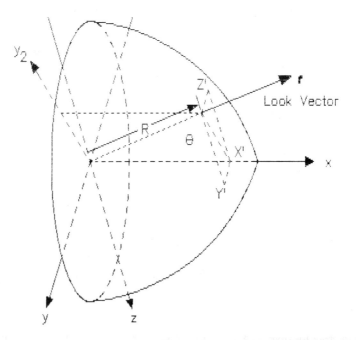

Fig. 8.7 Three-Dimensional Components of the Point of Intersection

8.3   CALCULATION OF THE E-VECTOR COMPONENTS

Now that we have solved for the intersection point (X', Y', Z'), we can calculate the normal, N, to the surface at that point by taking the divergence of the shape function ($\mathbf{F}$):

$$\mathbf{F} = xi + y^2 j + z^2 k \qquad (8.2)$$
$$\mathbf{N} = \nabla \cdot \mathbf{F} = i + 2Y'j + 2Z'k$$

We obtain the incidence angle, θ, from the dot product of the unit vector of the ray, $\mathbf{r}$, and the normal vector, $\mathbf{N}$, from (8.2):

$$
\begin{aligned}
\cos\theta &= \frac{\mathbf{r} \cdot \mathbf{N}}{|\mathbf{r}|\ |\mathbf{N}|} \\
&= \frac{(L_x i + L_y j + L_z k)\,(i + 2Y'j + 2Z'k)}{\left(1 + 4Y'^2 + 4Z'^2\right)^{1/2}} \\
&= \frac{\left(L_x + 2L_y Y' + 2L_z Z'\right)}{\left(1 + 4Y'^2 + 4Z'^2\right)^{1/2}}
\end{aligned}
\qquad (8.3)
$$

where L_x, L_y, and L_z are the direction cosines of the look vector, or ray, $\mathbf{r}$.

As shown in Figure 8.8, the look vector and normal vector uniquely determine the unit vectors for the parallel component (in the plane of the page) and the perpendicular component (out of the plane of the page). The unit vector for the electric field component perpendicular to the plane of incidence is given by

$$\mathbf{e}_\perp = \frac{\mathbf{N} \times \mathbf{r}}{|\mathbf{N}|\ \sin\theta} \qquad (8.4)$$

and the unit vector for the electric field component parallel to the plane of incidence is

$$\mathbf{e}_\| = \mathbf{e}_\perp \times \mathbf{r} \qquad (8.5)$$

The term "parallel" to the plane of incidence may be misleading. Note that the parallel component is defined by the look vector and the perpendicular vector. We use the normal to the surface only indirectly (through the perpendicular vector) in calculating the parallel vector. Note also that the direction of

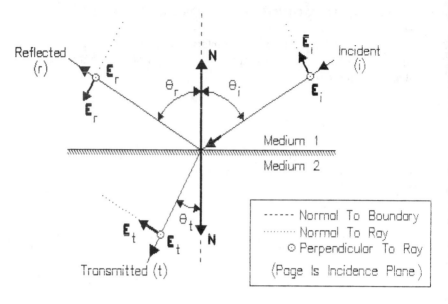

Fig. 8.8 Arbitrary Polarization States at a Boundary

the perpendicular vector in Figure 8.8 is constant, but the direction of the parallel vector changes for both reflection and transmission.

The E-vector is then decomposed into parallel (tangential) and perpendicular (normal) components with magnitudes determined by taking the dot products of the unit vectors with the E-vector.

$$| \mathbf{E}_\perp | = \mathbf{E} \cdot \mathbf{e}_\perp \tag{8.6}$$

$$| \mathbf{E}_\parallel | = \mathbf{E} \cdot \mathbf{e}_\parallel \tag{8.7}$$

If the incoming (or outgoing) signal is elliptically polarized, the above decomposition can be used with little modification. As shown in Figure 8.9, a right, circularly polarized wave incident is reflected as a left, elliptically polarized wave and transmitted as a right, elliptically polarized wave. This is a general case. As will be seen in later chapters, the reflected wave may be linearly polarized, or there may be no transmitted wave.

Figure 8.10 shows the general states of linear, elliptical, and circular polarizations. The waves are all traveling in the $+x$ direction (out of the page).

For the case of linear polarization, the field is given by

$$E_z = E_1 \sin (\omega t - \beta x)$$

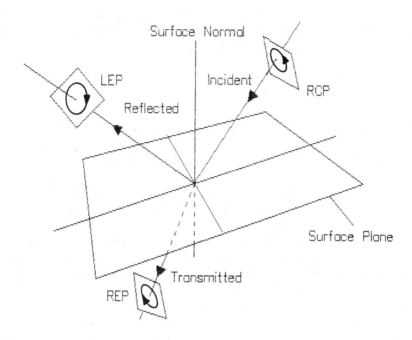

Fig. 8.9 Reflection and Transmission of a Right, Circularly Polarized Field

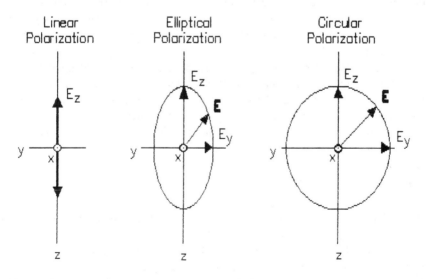

Fig. 8.10 General Polarization States

In general, however, the electric field traveling in the $+x$ direction may have components in both the z and y directions. The general expressions for the E-vector in terms of z and y components are

$$E_z = E_1 \sin (\omega t - \beta x)$$
$$E_y = E_2 \sin (\omega t - \beta x + \delta)$$

The two equations above describe the instantaneous field:

$$\mathbf{E} = \mathbf{z}\, E_1 \sin (\omega t - \beta x) + \mathbf{y}\, E_2 \sin (\omega t - \beta x + \delta) \tag{8.8}$$

The next chapter will present the polarization ellipse in more detail. Suffice it to say that a circularly polarized incident wave can be transmitted or reflected in virtually any polarization state.

We can handle the arbitrarily polarized wave through a repeated application of the process for linear polarization. Both of the elliptical components are decomposed into their respective parallel and perpendicular components. In the most general case, we have obtained four vectors to scale and recombine to form the total reflected and transmitted waves.

The general polarization case really underscores the major themes of this chapter. The point of intersection of the look vector with the radome surface and the normal vector at that point dictates how the incoming E-vector will be modified for transmission and reflection. For a circularly symmetric radome, all points of intersection for any angle off boresight will have the same angle of incidence, but the E-field decomposition can vary substantially from point to point, as Figure 8.11 shows.

The number of relative phase angles (deltas) among the different vectors also indicates that an algorithm calculating radome transmission characteristics must keep an accurate track of phase. While differences in the magnitude of the transmission or reflection coefficients can cause a rotation of the polarization ellipse, rotations due to phase shifts among E-field components are much more common and pronounced.

8.4 ANALYSIS

This section illustrates the procedure with several FORTRAN subroutines. This section also presents some typical data.

Listing #1 shows the program INCIDE. This program takes the following inputs: the radome length C, and the look vector to the point of interest (XLK, YLK, ZLK) and outputs; the point of intersection with the radome surface (XPR, YPR, ZPR) and the angle of incidence RAD.

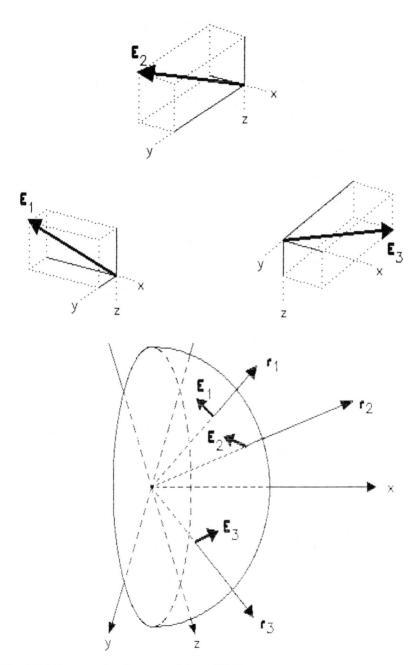

Fig. 8.11 Rectangular Decomposition of E-Vectors

LISTING #1

```
        PROGRAM INCIDE
C
C       THIS PROGRAM GENERATES THE INTERSECTION POINT
C       AND ANGLE OF INCIDENCE FOR A GIVEN RADOME
        LENGTH ( C )
C
        WRITE(*,*) ' ENTER RADOME LENGTH (M) '
        READ(*,*) C
C
        OPEN( 1, FILE = 'RAD.DAT' )
C
        DO 10 I = 0, 90
            AZ = FLOAT( I ) / 57.296
            ZLK = 0.0
            XLK = COS( AZ )
            YLK = SIN( AZ )
            CALL RADOME( C, XLK, YLK, ZLK, XPR, YPR, ZPR,
            RAD )
            WRITE( 1, * ) XPR, ' , ' , YPR, ' , ' , RAD*57.296, ' , '
            ENDIF
    10  CONTINUE
C
        STOP
        END
C
        SUBROUTINE RADOME( C, XLK, YLK, ZLK, XPR, YPR, ZPR,
        RAD )
C
C       ***** SINE & COSINE OF LOOK ANGLE.
C
        CTHETA = XLK
        STHETA = SQRT( ABS( 1.0 - CTHETA * CTHETA ) )
C
C       ***** INTERSECTION POINT BETWEEN LOOK VECTOR AND
        RADOME.
C
        IF ( CTHETA.NE.0.0 ) GO TO 1
            XPR = 0.0
            GO TO 3
```

```
1    IF ( STHETA.NE.0.0 ) GO TO 2
         XPR = C
         GO TO 3
2    T = STHETA / CTHETA
     T = T * T
     X = ( -1.0 + SQRT( 1.0 + 4.0 * C * T ) ) / ( 2.0 * T )
     XPR = ABS( X )
3    IF ( XPR.EQ.0.0 ) R = SQRT( C )
     IF ( XPR.EQ.0.0 ) GO TO 4
         R = XPR / CTHETA
4    YPR = YLK * R
     ZPR = ZLK * R
C
C        ***** CALCULATE NORMAL TO RADOME SURFACE AT
     INTERSECTION.
C
     DMAG = SQRT( 1.0 + 4.0 * YPR * YPR + 4.0 * ZPR * ZPR )
     XN = 1.0 / DMAG
     YN = 2.0 * YPR / DMAG
     ZN = 2.0 * ZPR / DMAG
     CRAD = DOTPR( XLK,YLK,ZLK,XN,YN,ZN )
     SRAD = SQRT( ABS( 1.0 - CRAD * CRAD ) )
     RAD = ARCSIN( SRAD )
C
     RETURN
     END
```

We encounter a wide range of angles of incidence in typical radomes. For several radome shape factors ranging from a very blunt missile radome to a pointed fighter radome, the look angle will be scanned from 0° to 90°. The calculation of the point of intersection and normals at this point will produce a map of the possible range of angles of incidence.

Figure 8.12 shows several radome cross sections with the length factor *C* ranging from 1 to 5 (arbitrary units). The angle of incidence and normal vector are shown only on the outermost surface for clarity.

Let us consider the radome shapes in Figure 8.12. As the look vector sweeps from 0° to 90°, the angles of incidence become those shown in Figure 8.13. Notice how rapidly the angle of incidence varies across the tip of the radome (theta = 0). Later chapters will prove that the smaller the angle of incidence, the better. At normal incidence, the E-vector is completely parallel to the radome surface, which makes decomposition unnecessary.

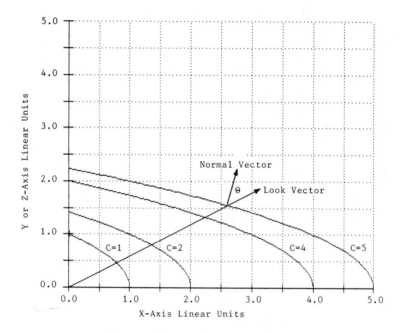

Fig. 8.12 Radome Shape Function for Various Shaping Coefficients

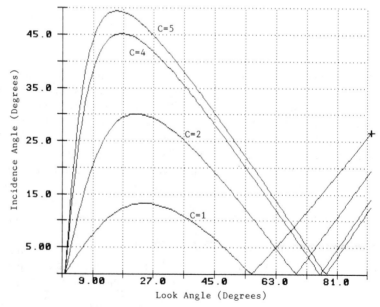

Fig. 8.13 Radome Surface Incidence Angle as a Function of Look Angle

The calculation of the perpendicular and parallel unit vectors at the point of intersection is important enough to warrant an example, even though this calculation is not as easy to visualize as the angle of incidence. Listing #2 presents the subroutine NORMAL. Notice how the routines work with unit vectors, and how the cross products are defined in terms of right-handed and left-handed conventions.

LISTING #2

```
C   ---------------------------------------------------------------------------------------
C                       SUBROUTINE "NORMAL"
C
C   THIS SUBROUTINE CALCULATES THE UNIT VECTORS
C   PARALLEL AND PERPENDICULAR TO THE PLANE
C   DEFINED BY UNIT LOOK VECTOR L AND UNIT
C   SURFACE NORMAL N.
C
C   AUTHOR: KURT E. HILDEBRANT
C
C
C   INPUTS:      XL,YL,ZL = UNIT LOOK VECTOR COMPONENTS.
C               XN,YN,ZN = UNIT SURFACE NORMAL
C                          COMPONENTS.
C
C   OUTPUTS:  VX,VY,VZ = VERTICAL (PARALLEL) UNIT VECTOR
C                          COMPONENTS.
C               HX,HY,HZ = HORIZONTAL (PERPENDICULAR)
C                          COMPONENTS.
C   ---------------------------------------------------------------------------------------
C
      SUBROUTINE NORMAL( XL,YL,ZL,XN,YN,ZN,VX,VY,VZ,HX,
      HY,HZ )
C
C   ***** L X N.
C
      CALL CROSSP( XL,YL,ZL,XN,YN,ZN,XLCN,YLCN,ZLCN )
C
C   ***** L * N = COS( THETA ).
C
      CTHETA = DOTPR( XL,YL,ZL,XN,YN,ZN )
      STHETA = SQRT( ABS( 1.0 - CTHETA * CTHETA ) )
C
C   ***** HORZ = L X N / SIN( THETA ).
```

```
C
    HX = XLCN / STHETA
    HY = YLCN / STHETA
    HZ = ZLCN / STHETA
C
C ***** VERT = H X L.
C
    CALL CROSSP( HX,HY,HZ,XL,YL,ZL,VX,VY,VZ )
    RETURN
    END
C
```

8.5 SUMMARY

At this point, we have established all the geometric relationships required to determine radome transmission, including the calculation of the following parameters:

- The point of intersection of the look vector with the radome surface;
- The normal and tangential components of the electric field at the intersection boundary;
- The angles and path lengths of the ray traveling through the media of the radome;
- The possible range of the angles of incidence for several different radomes.

The calculation of the transmission and its subsequent application to both single-layer and multilayer radomes is addressed in the following chapters.

Chapter 9

Transmission Modeling Techniques

This chapter presents the concepts and algorithm for calculating the transmission characteristics of a multilayered radome. We will introduce very fundamental electrostatic concepts and proceed to relatively complicated boundary relationships, which will enable us to compute the steady-state complex radome reflection and transmission coefficients. The reader need not have a complete understanding of this chapter in order to use or implement this modeling technique. Rather, this chapter is intended for the more advanced reader who wishes to gain a deeper insight into the methods presented in subsequent chapters.

The modeling technique presented here is analogous to the Smith chart. With the aid of the Smith chart, we can reduce a large and complicated electrical network to a net equivalent impedance. As with a Smith chart, the radome modeling method is a steady-state solution. The transient response characteristics are negligible, but they can be calculated with the radome equivalent of a bounce diagram. The discussion of the radome's transient behavior is presented to give the reader a better intuitive feel for the modeling technique, and will allow the advanced user to calculate the dissipated power and electric field intensity in individual layers of a multilayered radome.

Therefore, the objective is to calculate an equivalent impedance for a single or multilayered radome. This calculation can be envisioned as the reduction of the air-radome-air system to an equivalent half-space system, where one medium is free space and the other medium has the composite radome characteristics. The "equivalent material" may or may not be physically realizable. The equivalent impedance, expressed as a complex permittivity, will be used to calculate the steady-state reflection and transmission coefficients.

9.1 FUNDAMENTALS

As the ratio of the electric field to the magnetic field, the value and properties of the electrostatic impedance are completely determined by the intrinsic characteristics of the material in which the wave travels. Just as free space has an electric field permittivity and a magnetic field permeability determining field behavior in free space, so do all materials. For these materials, (9.1) gives the impedance where all quantities may be complex.

$$Z = (\mu/\epsilon)^{1/2} \qquad\qquad (9.1)$$

where

μ = permeability
ϵ = permittivity

Because most materials have relative magnetic field permeabilities very close to 1.0, we will drop μ and consider only variations with relative electric field permittivity, ϵ_r. Under these constraints, the speed of light in a medium is given by

$$v = c/(\epsilon_r)^{1/2} \qquad\qquad (9.2)$$

where

c = absolute speed of light
ϵ_r = relative permittivity

Note that in the equation relating wavelength and frequency in a medium to the velocity of propagation, (9.3) still holds true even if the medium is not free space. In media other than free space, the frequency of a signal remains constant and the wavelength changes according to (9.4).

$$c = \lambda F \qquad\qquad (9.3)$$

where

λ = wavelength in free space
F = frequency

$$\lambda' = v/F = \lambda/(\epsilon_r)^{1/2} \qquad\qquad (9.4)$$

where λ' is the wavelength in the medium.

Figure 9.1 shows the general half-space diagram, with the region above the boundary being free space and the region below the boundary having arbitrary permittivity.

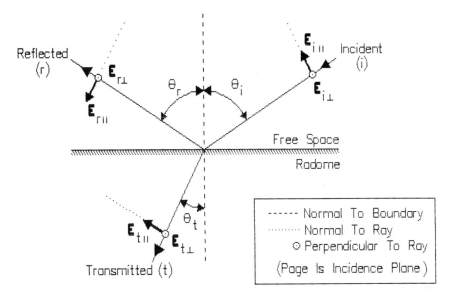

Fig. 9.1 Interactions at the Radome Boundary

We can show that the angle of reflection is equal to the angle of incidence. The angle of transmission is related to the angle of incidence by Snell's law, stated in (9.5).

$$\sin(\theta_t) = (\mu_1\epsilon_1/\mu_2\epsilon_2)^{1/2}\sin(\theta_i) \tag{9.5}$$

where

θ_i = angle of incidence
θ_t = angle of transmission (refraction)

By applying field continuity relationships at the boundary, it is possible to derive reflection coefficients for both the parallel and perpendicular components of the incident wave. The reflection coefficients presented here assume that there is no static charge at the boundary. It is not difficult to account for a static charge density at the boundary, but the equations for the reflection coefficients do get more complicated in form. Equations (9.6) and (9.7) present the reflection equation coefficients for the parallel and perpendicular electric field components, respectively. These are the Fresnel reflection coefficients.

$$\rho_\| = (Z_2c_t - Z_1c_i)/(Z_1c_i + Z_2c_t) \tag{9.6}$$
$$\rho_\perp = (Z_2c_i - Z_1c_t)/(Z_2c_i + Z_1c_t) \tag{9.7}$$

where

$$c_i = \cos\theta_i$$
$$c_t = \cos\theta_t$$
$$\rho_\parallel = \text{parallel reflection coefficient}$$
$$\rho_\perp = \text{perpendicular reflection coefficient}$$

For the case in which both media are lossless, nonmagnetic dielectrics, we can express (9.6) and (9.7) as

$$\rho_\parallel = \frac{-(\epsilon_2/\epsilon_1)\cos\theta_i + [(\epsilon_2/\epsilon_1) - \sin^2\theta_i]^{1/2}}{(\epsilon_2/\epsilon_1)\cos\theta_i + [(\epsilon_2/\epsilon_1) - \sin^2\theta_i]^{1/2}} \qquad (9.8)$$

$$\rho_\perp = \frac{\cos\theta_i - [(\epsilon_2/\epsilon_1) - \sin^2\theta_i]^{1/2}}{\cos\theta_i + [(\epsilon_2/\epsilon_1) - \sin^2\theta_i]^{1/2}} \qquad (9.9)$$

The reflection coefficients have some interesting characteristics, which are best illustrated graphically. Figure 9.2 illustrates the reflection coefficient magnitudes and phases for various lossless media. Note that the perpendicular component always experiences a 180° phase shift. The parallel component's phase shift depends on whether the angle of incidence is greater than the Brewster angle, which is discussed below.

Figure 9.3 presents similar data for lossy media. The loss factor for a medium is usually expressed as a *loss tangent*. The loss tangent is the ratio of the real part of the permittivity to the imaginary part. Typical loss tangents are less than 0.02 for common radome materials. In Figure 9.3, the phase can take values other than ± 180°. The smallest loss tangent in Figure 9.3 is 0.17 (tangent(10°)). For loss tangents encountered in commonly used materials, the effects of the real part of the permittivity on the phase and magnitude of the reflection coefficients are difficult to show graphically because they are so small. Hence, the radome may be considered lossless for modeling purposes.

Although it is not directly related to the modeling technique, another physical phenomenon associated with boundary analysis is the *Brewster angle*, or polarizing angle. This effect will be significant in Chapter 11, where we present complete radome analyses. However, it suffices to say here that the Brewster phenomenon affects only the parallel component of an incident electric field. If the angle of incidence is equal to the Brewster angle, the parallel component of the wave is totally transmitted into the second medium.

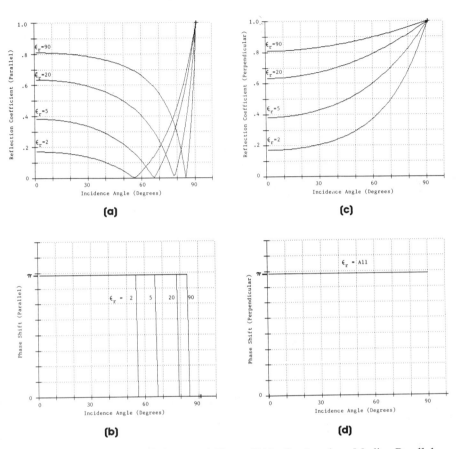

Fig. 9.2 Reflection Coefficients and Phase Shifts for Lossless Media, Parallel and Perpendicular Polarization

The perpendicular field component exhibits a similar behavior commonly called the *critical angle*. However, the situation for the perpendicular component is much more complex. When the angle of incidence is equal to or greater than the critical angle, the wave is said to be completely internally reflected. This means that the wave will be bound to the boundary, decaying exponentially away from the interface. This decay produces a very undesirable surface wave in the media with the smaller relative permittivity.

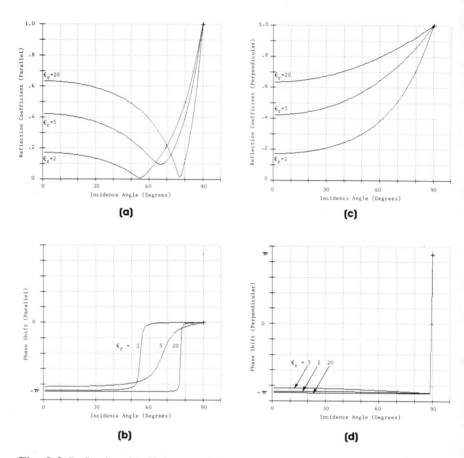

Fig. 9.3 Reflection Coefficients and Phase Shifts for Lossy Media, Parallel and Perpendicular Polarization

The relationship between the reflection coefficient and the transmission coefficient is frequently a source of confusion. If the reflection coefficient is defined as the ratio of the reflected wave to the incident wave, then the transmission coefficient is one plus the reflection coefficient.

$$\tau = \rho + 1$$

where τ is the transmission coefficient.

Even though the previous relationship seems very counterintuitive, it follows directly from the continuity of electric and magnetic field relationships at a boundary and the definition of the intrinsic media impedances.

The continuity relationships for the electric and magnetic fields at a boundary are

$$E_i + E_r = E_t$$
$$H_i + H_r = H_t$$

The definitions of the intrinsic media impedances dictate

$$E_i/H_i = Z_1$$
$$E_t/H_t = Z_2$$
$$E_r/H_r = -Z_1$$

These relationships are illustrated in Figure 9.4. Note that the change in sign on the reflected component is physically due to a reversal in direction of propagation.

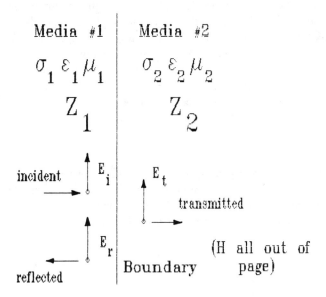

Fig. 9.4 Continuity Relationships at the Boundary

The transmission coefficient is defined as

$$\tau = E_t/E_i$$

and the reflection coefficient is defined as

$$\rho = E_r/E_i$$

Therefore, the field continuity and intrinsic impedance relationships can be manipulated to yield

$$\tau = (2Z_2)/(Z_1 + Z_2) = [(Z_2 - Z_1) + (Z_1 + Z_2)] / (Z_1 + Z_2)$$
$$= \text{transmitted wave / incident wave}$$
$$\rho = (Z_2 - Z_1)/(Z_1 + Z_2)$$
$$= \text{reflected wave / incident wave}$$

From the equations above, we can see that the transmission coefficient is one plus the reflection coefficient.

9.2 ALGORITHM

This section presents and explains the algorithm, which consists of several basic parts. The first part uses Snell's law and the angles of incidence and transmission to calculate the path lengths and angles through the radome. This is essentially *optical ray tracing*. We then use the path data, the characteristic impedance of the individual media, and the reflection coefficients to calculate the total steady-state impedance of the radome. The equivalent impedance of the radome will then allow us to treat the radome-air interface as a single junction, with reflection and transmission coefficients calculated in the usual manner.

9.2.1 Path Calculations

Figure 9.5 presents the planar radome structure with the ray-trace path. The angle of incidence, θ_i, from air onto the radome is known. The first loop in the program uses θ_i and Snell's law to calculate θ_t, which, in turn, is the incidence angle for the next surface. The path length in the medium is given by (9.11).

$$L_p = L_n/\cos\theta_t \qquad\qquad (9.11)$$

where
$$L_p = \text{path length}$$
$$L_n = \text{normal length}$$

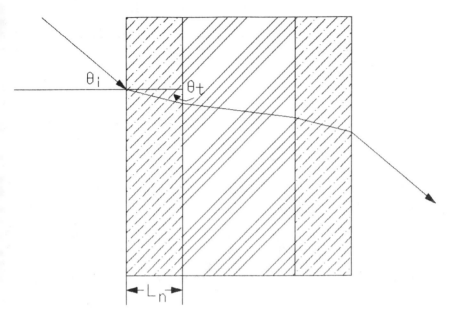

Fig. 9.5 Optical Ray Trace Path

9.2.2 Equivalent Impedance

When a plane wave initially contacts the multilayered dielectric surface, a portion is transmitted and a portion is reflected. When the portion that was transmitted strikes the next surface, the process is repeated. Figure 9.6 shows this process graphically. The transition time for the wave inside the radome is roughly 50 ps, and the reflections die quickly. This leaves the radome with two traveling waves: the transmission wave traveling to the right and the reflection wave traveling to the left. In each layer of the radome, there is a wave composed of the transmission wave and its reflection, plus the reflection wave and its reflection from the other side of the layer.

The reflection and transmission at any particular interface are a function of the material properties and the angles involved, and all layers have waves coming in both sides—that is, all but one. The far layer is air and is considered to be of infinite extent, so there is no input from that side. Therefore, the reflected wave begins at this boundary and has a value determined by the magnitude of the transmitted wave in the last layer and the reflection coefficient at the air-radome interface.

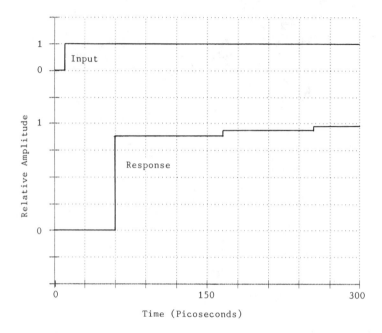

Time (Picoseconds)

Fig. 9.6 Radome Response to Step Input

Once again, we use the transmission line analogy. Figure 9.7 shows a general terminated transmission line. In our case, however, Z_1 represents the impedance of free space (377 Ω), and Z_0 is equal to the impedance of the final radome layer and may be complex. A material that has a real component in its relative permittivity is lossy. Therefore, it is more correct to say that free space has an impedance of j377 Ω. The load is at $x = 0$, and positive x is measured to the left.

At a point that is a distance X_1 from the load, we call the voltage between the wires $\mathbf{V}_i$ and the current in one of the wires due to the incident wave $\mathbf{I}_i$. We accordingly let the wave traveling to the left be described by $\mathbf{V}_r$ and $\mathbf{I}_r$. The total voltage at distance X_1 is the sum of the voltages $\mathbf{V}_i$ and $\mathbf{V}_r$. That is,

$$\mathbf{V} = \mathbf{V}_i + \mathbf{V}_r$$

where $\mathbf{V}$ is the total voltage.

At the load, with $x = 0$:

$$\mathbf{V}_r / \mathbf{V}_i = \rho_v$$

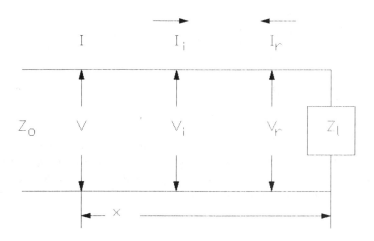

Fig. 9.7 Terminated Transmission Line

Thus, the total complex voltage is

$$\mathbf{V} = V_I\exp(\gamma x) + \rho_v\exp(-\gamma x)$$

where
$$\gamma = \alpha + j\beta$$
$$\beta = \text{wavenumber } 2\pi/\lambda$$

The sum of the currents is

$$\mathbf{I} = \mathbf{I}_i + \mathbf{I}_r$$

Thus,

$$\mathbf{I} = I_0\exp(-j\delta)[\exp(\gamma x) + \rho_I\exp(-\gamma x)]$$

The reflection coefficient for voltage can also be expressed as

$$\mathbf{V}_r / \mathbf{V}_i = (Z_1 - Z_0) / (Z_1 + Z_0) = \rho_v$$

The ratio of the total voltages to the total currents is the impedance at point X_1. This impedance becomes the load impedance for the next layer, and the process continues until all layers have been included.

For lossless media, the impedance at X_1 can be expressed as

$$Z_x = Z_0 \left[\frac{Z_1 + jZ_0 \tan(\beta x)}{Z_0 + jZ_1 \tan(\beta x)} \right] \tag{9.12}$$

where

$x = L_p$, the path length

$\beta = 2\pi/\lambda'$, the wavenumber in the medium

This expression is the normal equation for the impedance at a point distance x from the load on a lossless transmission line. The transmission line equations are equivalent to the radome impedance equations for normal incidence. If we substitute the Fresnel reflection coefficients for the voltage reflection coefficient in the above derivation, we obtain an equation for the impedance for the parallel and perpendicular components:

$$Z_\perp = Z_0 \frac{Z_1 \cos_i + Z_0 \cos_t \operatorname{ctanh}(\beta x)}{Z_0 \cos_t + Z_1 \cos_i \operatorname{ctanh}(\beta x)}$$

$$Z_\parallel = Z_0 \frac{Z_1 \cos_t + Z_0 \cos_i \operatorname{ctanh}(\beta x)}{Z_0 \cos_i + Z_1 \cos_t \operatorname{ctanh}(\beta x)}$$

where

$\cos_i$ = incident angle cosine

$\cos_t$ = transmitted angle cosine

ctanh = complex hyperbolic tangent

These are the general impedance expressions that will be used in the program.

Mathematically, this operation is very similar to building a Smith chart. Although we need not thoroughly understand the Smith chart in order to understand the modeling technique, we occasionally refer to the chart in this chapter because it is a useful analogy for those readers familiar with this graphical technique. The two differences in the model are the following: the presence of the cosines of the angles of transmission and incidence in the reflection coefficients; the changing of the wavelength in the different media.

In Chapter 10, we will present an example case using both a Smith chart and the model developed in this chapter. The example will serve to correlate the results of the two methods. At this point, however, the equations and techniques developed in this chapter can be combined into a program that will calculate the perpendicular and parallel reflection coefficients of a radome as a function of incidence angle, layer thicknesses, and layer permittivities.

9.3 ANALYSIS

Listing #3, which appears at the end of this chapter, presents the program SMITH. It is designed to write out data that will be used for a look-up table. Although this program is included in Appendix B along with other radome-related subroutines, it is also presented at the end of this chapter so the reader may refer to it conveniently while continuing through this section. Examination of the various loops in the program as they are discussed will result in a thorough understanding of the technique, because the reader will recognize the FORTRAN versions of the equations presented in this chapter in the program.

SMITH (as in the Smith chart) calculates the steady-state transmission and reflection coefficients for lossless media. Although the Smith chart uses VSWR (voltage standing wave ratio) and movement along circles of constant VSWR, VSWR is not used explicitly in the algorithm. Instead, the routine directly calculates apparent impedances at the layer boundaries. As mentioned previously, disregarding losses simplifies matters considerably.

After we enter data and initialize constants, the first loop calculates the angles of transmission using the angle of incidence as the "initial condition." With the angles of transmission calculated, this loop can also calculate the path length in the media.

These data allow us to build the Smith chart. The next loop starts at the last radome boundary. This is the boundary from which there is no reflected component. The purpose of this loop is to calculate the total apparent impedance for the multilayered radome. For the first iteration, the impedance is set to that of free space. Thereafter, the impedance is set to the total impedance seen to that boundary. It is important to note that even though the media impedances are not complex, the total radome impedance may be complex due to the phase delays incurred in the transition of layers. It is also interesting to note that different impedances must be calculated for both parallel and perpendicular components. It is apparent that the transmission function of the radome is heavily dependent on the engagement geometry and signal polarization.

Once we know the composite radome impedance, we can evaluate the Fresnel reflection coefficients. The transmission coefficients are calculated as

$$\tau_\parallel = (\rho + one)(\cos_i/\cos_t)$$
$$\tau_\perp = (\rho + one)$$

If we desire only the power transmission coefficients, we can obtain the magnitude of the transmission coefficient squared:

$$|\tau^2| = 1.0 - |\rho^2|$$

for either polarization.

9.4   SUMMARY

This chapter presented the Smith chart analogy and boundary relationships. Several subtleties of the modeling method, mostly relating to radomes with an even number of layers, have been left to later chapters where they can be explained by examples.

LISTING #3

```
        PROGRAM SMITH
C
C          THIS PROGRAM CALCULATES THE TRANSMISSION
C          COEFFICIENT FOR A MULTILAYERED RADOME.
C
        REAL WL,RAD,PI,TWOPI,DTOR,THE(10,2),THETA,
        LEN,COSI,COST
C
        COMPLEX ZO, J, RHOPARA, RHOPERP, Z_SPACE, T1, T2,
    $   CTANH, ZPHASE, MAT(10,5), ZT_PERP, ZT_PARA,
    $   ZL_PERP, ZL_PARA
C
        INTEGER I, N, K, ANGLE, KP1
C
C          INITIALIZE CONSTANTS
C
        PI     = 3.141592654
        TWOPI = 2.0 * PI
        DTOR   = PI / 180.0
C
C          INITIALIZE J = SQRT( -1 )
C
        J = ( 0.0 , 1.0 )
C
C          INITIALIZE FREE SPACE IMPEDANCE
C
        Z_SPACE = ( 0.0 , 376.7 )
C
        OPEN(1,FILE = 'PERP.TAU')
        OPEN(2,FILE = 'PARA.TAU')
C
C
        WRITE(*,*) 'INPUT NUMBER OF LAYERS   '
```

```
C
C        INPUT NUMBER OF LAYERS ( < 10 )
         READ(*,*) N
C
C        READ PARAMETERS
C
         MAT( N + 1 , 1 ) = (1.0, 0.0)
         MAT( N + 1 , 4 ) = Z_SPACE
         MAT( N + 1 , 2 ) = 0.0
C
C        REL. PERMITTIVITY OF MEDIA        MAT(X,1)
C        NORMAL DEPTH OF MEDIA             MAT(X,2)
C        WAVELENGTH IN MEDIA              MAT(X,3)
C        IMPEDANCE OF MEDIA               MAT(X,4)
C        PATH LENGTH IN MEDIA             MAT(X,5)
C        INCIDENT ANGLE COSINE            THE(X,1)
C        TRANSMITTED ANGLE COSINE         THE(X,2)
C
         WRITE(*,*) 'ENTER OPERATING WAVELENGTH ( M )   '
         READ(*,*) WL
C
         DO 100 I=1,N
         WRITE (*,*) ' '
         WRITE(*,*) 'LAYER NUMBER ',I
         WRITE(*,*) 'INPUT;'
         WRITE(*,*) 'RELATIVE PERMITTIVITY '
         READ(*,*) MAT( I , 1 )
         WRITE(*,*) 'NORMAL LENGTH '
         READ(*,*)LEN
         MAT (I,2) = CMPLX (LEN,0.0)
C
  100    CONTINUE
C
C        THIS LOOP CALCULATES THE WAVELENGTH IN THE
C        MEDIA AND THE IMPEDANCE OF THE MEDIA
C
         DO 50 I = 1 , N
            MAT( I , 3 ) = WL / CSQRT( MAT( I , 1 ) )
            MAT( I , 4 ) = Z_SPACE / CSQRT( MAT( I , 1 ) )
   50    CONTINUE
C
C
```

```
C     ********************************
C     *                              *
C     *     BEGIN MAJOR LOOPS        *
C     *                              *
C     ********************************
C
          DO 1000 ANGLE = 0 , 90
C
          RAD = REAL( ANGLE ) * DTOR
C
C         BEGIN CALCULATIONS BY CALCULATING RAY PATH
          LENGTHS AND ANGLES
C
          DO 200 K = 1 , N + 1
          IF ( K .EQ. 1 ) THEN
              THE( K , 1 ) = COS( RAD )
              THETA = SIN( RAD ) / SQRT( CABS( MAT( 1 , 1 ) ) )
          ELSE
              THE( K , 1 ) = SQRT( 1.0 - THETA * THETA )
              THETA = SQRT( CABS( MAT(K - 1,1) / MAT(K,1) ) ) *
          THETA
          ENDIF
C
          THE( K, 2 ) = SQRT( 1.0 - THETA * THETA )
          MAT( K, 5 ) = MAT( K, 2 ) / THE( K, 2 )
C
      200 CONTINUE
C
C         NOW DEVELOP TRANSMISSION LINE EQUIVALENT
C
          DO 300 K = N , 1 , -1
C
              KP1 = K + 1
              COSI = THE( KP1, 1 )
              COST = THE( KP1, 2)
C
              IF ( K .EQ. N ) THEN
                  ZL_PERP = Z_SPACE
                  ZL_PARA = Z_SPACE
              ELSE
                  ZL_PERP = ZT_PERP
                  ZL_PARA = ZT_PARA
              ENDIF
```

```
C
                ZO = MAT( K, 4 )
C
                ZPHASE = -J * TWOPI * MAT( K , 5 ) / MAT( K , 3 )
C
                IF ( CCOS( ZPHASE ) .EQ. 0.0 ) THEN
                    ZT_PERP = ZO * ZO * COST / ZL_PERP * COSI
                    ZT_PARA = ZO * ZO * COSI / ZL_PARA * COST
                ELSE
                    ZT_PERP = ZO*( (ZL_PERP*COSI +
                               ZO*COST*CTANH
                               (ZPHASE)) /
                               (ZO*COST + ZL_
                               PERP*COSI*CTANH
          &                    (ZPHASE)) )
C
                    ZT_PARA = ZO*( (ZL_PARA*COST +
                               ZO*COSI*CTANH
                               (ZPHASE)) /
                               (ZO*COSI + ZL_
                               PARA*COST*CTANH
          &                    (ZPHASE)) )
                ENDIF
C
     1000   CONTINUE
C
          COSI = THE( 1, 1 )
          COST = THE( 1, 2 )
C
          RHOPERP = ( ZT_PERP*COSI - Z_SPACE*COST )
          &              /( ZT_PERP*COSI + Z_SPACE*COST )
C
          RHOPARA = ( ZT_PARA*COST - Z_SPACE*COSI )
          &              /( ZT_PARA*COST + Z_SPACE*COSI )
C
          T1 = ( 1.0 - CABS( RHOPERP )**2 )
          T2 = ( 1.0 - CABS( RHOPARA )**2 )
C
          WRITE(1,*) CABS( T1 )
          WRITE(2,*) CABS( T2 )
C
     1000   CONTINUE
C
```

```
                CLOSE ( 1 )
                CLOSE ( 2 )
C
                STOP
                END
C
C               ---------------------------------------------------
C               COMPLEX HYPERBOLIC TANGENT
C               ---------------------------------------------------
C
                COMPLEX FUNCTION CTANH( U )
C
                COMPLEX U
                REAL ZR, ZI
C
                ZR  =  2.0 * REAL( U )
                ZI  =  2.0 * AIMAG( U )
C
                CTANH  =  CMPLX(SINH( ZR ), SIN( ZI )) /
           &            CMPLX(COSH( ZR ) + COS( ZI ), 0.0)
C
                RETURN
C
```

REFERENCE

1. Kraus, John D., and Keith Carver, *Electromagnetics*, 2nd Ed., New York: McGraw-Hill, 1973, Chapter 12.

Chapter 10
Application to Single-Layer Radomes

In the previous chapter, we derived the algorithm for calculating the steady-state transmission and reflection. Through the use of examples, we will show how the method is applied to single-layer radomes and some typical results.

The single-layer radome is the most common type of radome. The radome examined in this chapter will not have an antistatic layer, that will be left to the discussion of thin layers in the next chapter. The single-layer radome lends itself easily to analysis, and a great deal of information is available on them.

Chapter 8 discussed the importance of the engagement geometry. Chapter 9 presented the radome modeling technique. In this chapter, we will apply the results of the two previous chapters to the problem of single-layer radomes.

10.1 SINGLE-LAYER RADOME IN LOSSLESS MEDIA

In these examples, the radome material will be lossless. This means that the loss tangent is equal to zero, or equivalently, that the relative permittivity has no real component. This will simplify the analysis in several ways. If the relative permittivity has a real component, the angles of reflection and transmission will be complex. The interpretation of complex angles of transmission and reflection is mathematically cumbersome and computationally slow in a simulation, and is best avoided whenever possible. We see in (10.1) the general form of the equation used to calculate an impedance for a terminated line at point x.

$$Z_x = Z_0 \frac{Z_1 + Z_0 \tanh(\beta x)}{Z_0 + Z_1 \tanh(\beta x)} \tag{10.1}$$

Mathematically, if the relative permittivity is purely imaginary, then we can reduce the hyperbolic tangent in (10.1) via the trigonometric identity shown below to obtain (10.2).

$$\tanh(\beta x) = j\tan(\beta x) \tag{10.2}$$

$$Z_x = Z_0 \frac{Z_1 + jZ_0\tan(\beta x)}{Z_0 + jZ_1\tan(\beta x)}$$

In short, an analysis of lossless media is much more straightforward (and probably more informative) than the analysis of lossy media. Also, if the reader has a good understanding of the lossless case, he or she can analyze lossy media better.

Figure 10.1 shows the geometry for the single-layer radome, with the physical parameters as shown. As previously mentioned, we view the radome as being locally planar.

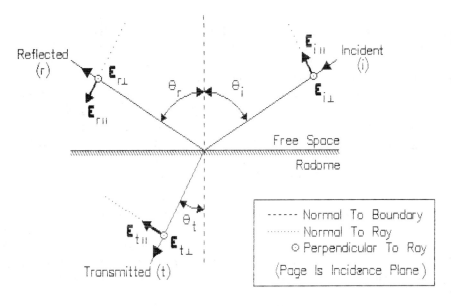

Fig. 10.1 Interactions at the Radome Boundary

Example 1 Normal Incidence

The case of normal incidence presents further simplification because the reflection coefficients for the parallel and perpendicular components are equal. The cosines in the Fresnel reflection coefficients are equal to 1.0 for normal incidence, giving the form of equation normally seen in transmission line calculations. Thus, we need not consider polarization. Returning to the transmission line analogy, Figure 10.2 presents the terminated transmission line bounce diagram with the magnitudes of various transmitted and reflected components.

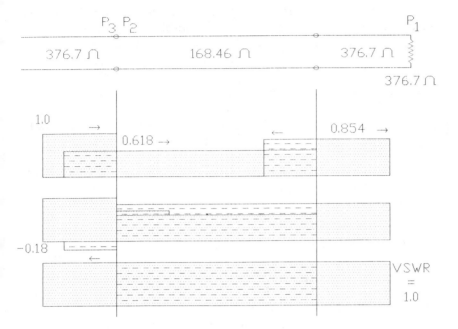

Fig. 10.2 Reflections on a Terminated Transmission Line

The impedance of the left and right sections of the line is that of free space (377 Ω), and the right section is terminated with a 377 Ω load. If the line terminated with a load has an impedance equal to that of the line, then no reflected wave will be at the load. The impedance of the center section is equal to the intrinsic impedance of the radome material.

$$Z' = Z_0/(\epsilon_r)^{1/2}$$

Both the left and right sections can be of arbitrary length. The center section has a length equal to the phase shift that the wave experiences in the layer. This phase shift is equal to 360° (path length/wavelength). For normal incidence, the path length through the media is equal to the normal depth of the media. The wavelength in the media is given by

$$v = c/(\epsilon_r)^{1/2}$$
$$\lambda' = v/F$$

where F is the frequency.

To continue with the example, let the operating frequency be 10 GHz, the relative permittivity be equal to 5.0, and the normal depth of the material be 1 cm. From these parameters, we make the following calculations: the transmission line has an impedance of $377/(5^{1/2}) = 168.6\ \Omega$; a phase shift due to transition of the layer is equal to $360\ \{1.0\ \text{cm}/[3.0\ \text{cm}/(5.0^{1/2})]\} = 268.33°$. The only values still needed to describe the transmission line completely are the reflection and transmission coefficients at the boundaries.

As previously mentioned, the forms of the Fresnel reflection coefficients are

$$\rho_{\parallel} = (Z_2 c_t - Z_1 c_i)/(Z_1 c_i + Z_2 c_t)$$

$$\rho_{\perp} = (Z_2 c_i - Z_1 c_t)/(Z_2 c_i + Z_1 c_t)$$

(10.3)

where
$$c_i = \cos\theta_i$$
$$c_t = \cos\theta_t$$

All quantities may be complex. For normal incidence, the cosines in the above equations are all equal to 1.0.

Table 10.1 lists the reflection and transmission coefficients at the boundaries. Note the sign reversal on the reflection coefficients when the boundary is crossed in the opposite direction. Also note that the transmission coefficient is 1.0 plus the reflection coefficient. The coefficients in this table represent those for the nonsteady-state or transient response and are applicable to constructing the bounce diagram of Figure 10.2. We determine these coefficients by applying the Fresnel equations found in (10.3) to the actual media impedances to obtain the value of the reflection coefficients, then solving for the transmission coefficients.

Table 10.1 Reflection and Transmission Coefficients

Media	Free Space	Radome Material		Free Space
Media Impendance (Ω)	376.7	168.46		376.7
Crossing Direction	$\rightarrow$	$\leftarrow$	$\rightarrow$	
Reflection Coefficient	−0.382	0.382	0.382	
Transmission Coefficient	0.618	1.382	1.382	

We obtain the steady-state transmission coefficient by first determining the composite impedance according to (10.2), solving for ρ according to (10.3), and solving for τ according to (9.10), which is given below:

$$\tau = \rho + 1$$

This equation results in a steady-state transmission coefficient of τ = 0.74.

We assume normal incidence for this example. In both the steady-state and transient cases, the cosines in the Fresnel equations are equal to 1.0, making the reflection coefficients for both polarizations equal.

We may now build the bounce diagram. The wave will be incident from the left, traveling to the right. If the incoming wave has an amplitude equal to 1 V, then at junction 1, 0.62 V will be transmitted and 0.38 V will be reflected. It is interesting to note that all realizable materials have a relative permeability greater than one. This means that the impedance of a material must always be less than that of free space. Therefore, the magnitude of the electric field must always be smaller in the radome material than in free space. Figure 10.2 illustrates the transmitted and reflected wave values as well as the arrival times at the junctions. Note the values for the VSWR shown in this figure. Because the transition time for the radome layer is so small, the reflections will not last for more than several cycles.

In order to reinforce the modeling method, we will solve the same problem on a Smith chart. Although some of the Smith chart calculations are superfluous, the exercise is very useful for those familiar with Smith charts. The Smith chart is shown in Figure 10.3.

As mentioned, the lengths of the lines on the right and left sides of Figure 10.2 are arbitrary. For this discussion, the lengths will be taken as zero, which leaves the simple circuit shown in Figure 10.4 for us to analyze.

We enter the Smith chart at point P where the normalized impedance is

$$Z_n = 377/168.6 = 2.236$$

The wavelength in the media is

$$3.0 \text{ cm}/(5.0^{1/2}) = 1.34 \text{ cm}$$

This means that for a layer 1 cm thick, the layer is 1.0 cm/1.34 cm = 0.746 wavelengths long. Because a complete circle of the Smith chart is half of a wavelength, we move 0.746 − 0.5 = 0.246 wavelengths clockwise on the Smith chart to point P_2, where the impedance is slightly reactive. If the layer

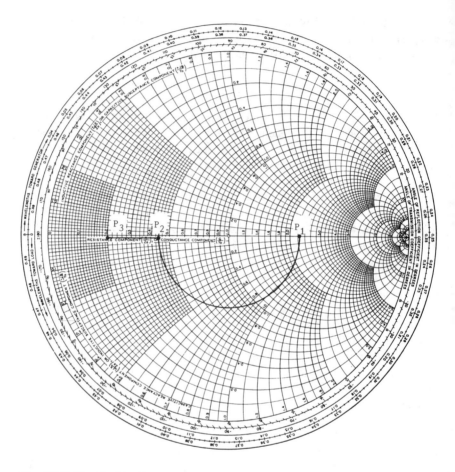

Fig. 10.3 The Smith Chart

thickness where chosen so that we move 1/4 wavelength around the chart, the normalized impedance at that point would be

$$Z = (1/2.236) = 0.44722$$

We must remember that circling the Smith chart 180° is equivalent to transforming the normalized impedance to a normalized addmitance.

At the point chosen for the example, 0.746 wavelengths around the Smith chart, we may calculate the impedance by evaluating (10.2). The point marked P_2 on the Smith chart has the following unnormalized impedance.

For simplicity, assume that the medium was 1/4 wavelength thick, and that the apparent impedance of the media was 75.4 Ω. As mentioned for the

$$Z = 168.6 \left[\frac{377 + j168.6 \tan(2\pi 0.746)}{168.6 + j377 \tan(2\pi 0.746)} \right]$$
$$= 168.6(0.44 \langle -2.57°)$$
$$= 74.18 \langle -2.57°$$

We may calculate the VSWR at the air-radome interface by multiplying the normalized impedance at P_2 by the ratio of the impedance of medium 1 to the impedance of air ($168.6/377 = 0.447$). This moves the impedance to point P_3:

$$P_3 = 0.447 (0.44 \langle -2.57°) = 0.1966 - j9.34E - 03$$

The VSWR at point P_3 can be directly read as 5.1.

Fig. 10.4 Single-Layer Radome Equivalent Circuit

case of normal incidence, the cosines in (10.3) are equal to 1, and the reflection coefficients can be directly evaluated:

$$\rho_\perp = (75.4 - 377)/(377 + 75.4)$$
$$= -0.666$$
$$\rho_\| = \rho_\perp$$

The transmission coefficient is

$$\tau_\perp = \tau_\| = \rho_\perp + 1 = 0.333$$

This is obviously a very low value for transmission.

In this simple example, however, most of the fundamental design philosophy for radomes is apparent. Interestingly, the VSWR circle in Figure 10.3 has a value equal to the reciprocal of the square root of the relative permittivity of the media. Ideally, the permittivity of the radome material should be kept as close as possible to that of air. If the radome material has a relatively high permittivity, as in this example, the material depth becomes very important. If the layer in the example had been 1/4 wavelength shorter, the apparent impedance would have been 377 Ω. The reflection and transmission coefficients would then have been

$$\rho = (377 - 377)/(377 + 377) = 0$$
$$\tau = \rho + 1 = 1$$

Example 2 Arbitrary Incidence

Now that we have considered normal incidence, we will expand the previous example to consider oblique incidence.

The effect on the Smith chart from changing the angle of incidence is graphically shown in Figure 10.5.

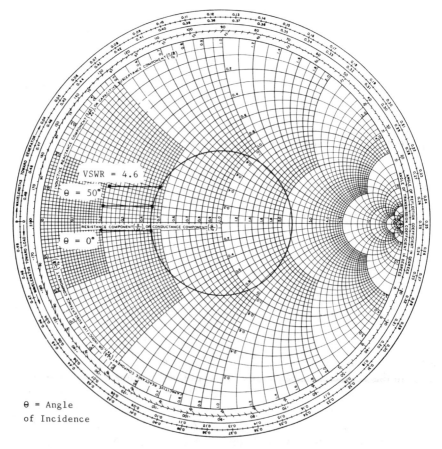

VSWR = 4.6

θ = 50°

θ = 0°

θ = Angle
of Incidence

Fig. 10.5 Smith Chart for Varying Angles of Incidence

The path length in the media has already been shown to be equal to

$$L_p = L_n/\cos\theta_t$$

We can calculate the angle of transmission from Snell's law. For the case of a wave incident on a surface from air, Snell's law becomes

$$\sin\theta_t = [1/(\epsilon_r^{1/2})]\sin\theta_i$$

Therefore, as the angle of incidence sweeps from 0° to 50°, the angle of transmission sweeps from 0° to 22°. As seen before, when moving from a region of low relative permittivity to one of high relative permittivity, the angle of transmission is less than the angle of incidence. The path length in the media with an incidence angle equal to 50° is 1.06 cm. This value gives a phase length for the media of 0.79 wavelengths, or 284.4°.

The different impedances obtained as the angle of incidence sweeps to 50° are shown in Figure 10.5. As the path length in the media becomes longer, the Smith chart is circled further in the clockwise direction. The VSWR is still calculated by renormalizing the impedance to that of free space (by multiplying by 168.6/377), which equates to a horizontal movement to the left.

For the example chosen, the effects of changing the angle of incidence are not too pronounced. However, the normal depth of the media and the relative impedance of the media are interrelated when we consider the effects of varying the angle of incidence. The relatively high permittivity of the media keeps the angle of transmission from getting too high. The normal thickness of the media determines how much the path length will change with angle of incidence; the longer the normal length, the greater the variation with angle of incidence.

10.2 FREQUENCY DEPENDENCY

Just as the apparent impedance of the radome varies with angle of incidence due to the change of path length, the phase length of the media also varies with the frequency of the wave. Figure 10.6 shows several plots of radome transmission as a function of incidence angle and frequency.

Note that although the transmission function is not very good, the transmission characteristics of the radome are relatively constant.

10.3 SUMMARY

Chapter 10 has shown how the transmission modeling method developed in Chapter 9 may be used to calculate the transmission coefficients as a function of the incidence angle. We expanded on the transmission line analogy and used the Smith chart to demonstrate graphically how the VSWR of the system varies as a function of the angle of incidence.

Note that the Brewster and critical angles posed no problem in the analysis of single-layer radomes. These effects do not occur in single-layer radomes. The Brewster effect was mentioned only in the polarization discussion for completeness. These and other interesting properties of multilayered radomes will be discussed in Chapter 11.

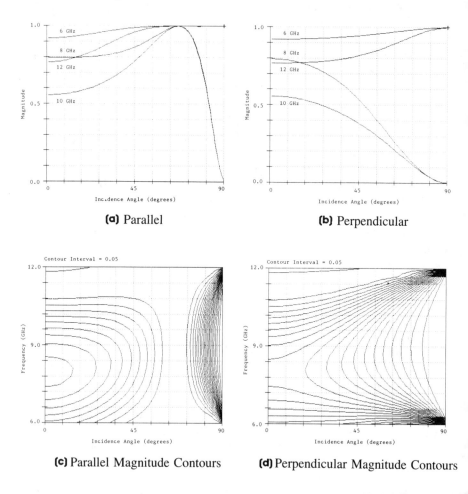

(a) Parallel   (b) Perpendicular

(c) Parallel Magnitude Contours   (d) Perpendicular Magnitude Contours

Fig. 10.6 Parallel and Perpendicular Transmission Coefficients

Chapter 11
Application to Multilayered Radomes

In the previous chapter, we presented the modeling method as it applies to single-layer radomes. The study of the single-layer radome shows the fundamental principles and interactions involved in radome analysis. Single-layer radomes offer moderately good transmission characteristics over a wide range of incidence angles. Perhaps more importantly, they offer relatively constant properties.

Multilayered radome behavior is much more complex. Multilayered radomes can be designed to offer much better transmission characteristics, but over a smaller range of frequencies and angles of incidence. Because their characteristics can change rapidly in small increments of incidence angle or frequency, multilayered radomes filter the signals passing through them to a much higher degree than do single-layer radomes.

11.1 RAY TRACING THROUGH MULTILAYERED RADOMES

The last chapter showed that the angle at which the wave finally exits the radome is equal to the angle of incidence for single-layer radomes. This fact is intuitively obvious. What is not so obvious is that the final angle of transmission is equal to the initial angle of incidence in all cases. Figure 11.1 presents a two-layer radome with parameters as marked. The initial angle of incidence is 30°, and the interim angles of transmission are as marked with the final angle of transmission equal to 30°.

A simple application of Snell's law can show that the final angle of transmission is equal to the initial angle of incidence. The angle of transmission can be tracked through the radome as

$$\sin\theta_i = (4/1)^{1/2}(6/4)^{1/2}(1/6)^{1/2}\sin\theta_t$$
$$\sin\theta_i = \sin\theta_t$$

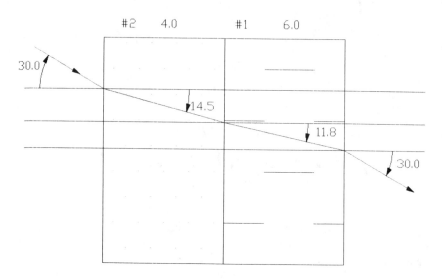

Fig. 11.1 Two-Layer Ray Trace Path

These results are not intuitively obvious, but the above application of Snell's law shows that for any radome structure, the final angle of transmission is equal to the initial angle of incidence.

What does this result say for the critical angle? Initially, the wave strikes a layer that must have a higher relative permittivity than free space; therefore, the critical angle condition cannot be met at the first interface. Just as in the single-layer case, the initial angle of transmission must be less than the initial angle of incidence. What the above exercise demonstrates is that regardless of the structure of the radome, the terms in the numerator and denominator under the square root must cancel. This is true even for lossy media, and this means that the critical angle condition cannot be reached for a multilayered structure.

11.2   QUARTER-WAVE MATCHING

Suppose we desire to maximize the transmission coefficient of a single-layer radome of arbitrary thickness (the thickness was chosen for strength or other mechanical considerations) by making a three-layer radome structure. How would we choose the relative impedance and thickness of the other two layers? Why not use a two-layer design?

Just as transmission lines can be matched to lines of a different impedance by using quarter-wave matching sections, so can radome materials. The situation for radome materials is, more accurately, a question of matching the air to a radome material and then back to the air again—which is the motivation for three-layer radomes.

However, before we discuss three-layer radomes and quarter-wave matching, we must determine what kind of match can be obtained with a two-layer system. Figure 11.2 shows the Smith chart on which we will work the two-layer problem.

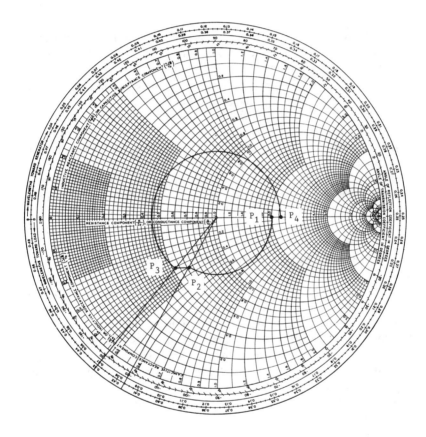

Fig. 11.2 Two-Layer Smith Chart

First, let us assume that layer #2 in Figure 11.1 is the layer we wish to match and that layer #1 is the layer the length and permittivity of which we can vary. We enter the Smith chart at P_1 where the normalized impedance is 2.0. As in the previous chapter, we let the frequency of interest be 10 GHz and the normal depth of the layer be 1.0 cm. With these parameters, the wavelength in the media is 3.0 cm/($4^{1/2}$) = 1.5 cm, and the phase length of the media is $2\pi(1.0/1.5)$ = $(4/3)\pi$ = 240°. Moving 60° around the Smith chart puts the normalized impedance at P_2 (0.62, − 0.4).

We must now choose the layer depth and normal length for layer #1. What is the design criterion? The ultimate goal is to leave the Smith chart with a VSWR of 1. In these examples, the only available motions on the Smith chart are to circle the chart (normalized impedance along a line), and to move horizontally (normalized impedance between lines). No movement occurs along lines of constant conductance, as in the classic stub tuner and double-stub tuner problems.

The lengths of the horizontal movements must add up to 1. Just as in the case of the angle of transmission equaling the angle of incidence, when we normalize and renormalize to the impedances of various media, the terms must cancel to 1.0 when the radome is exited. If the relative permittivity of layer #1 is higher than that of layer #2, then the initial horizontal movement (to renormalize to layer #1's impedance) will be to the left, taking the impedance to the outer VSWR circle in Figure 11.2. Conversely, if the relative permittivity of layer #1 is lower than that of layer #2, then the initial horizontal movement will be to the right, leaving the impedance at P_3 (for $\epsilon_{r1} = 6$).

In either case, the options are limited. To find the best length for the case of a higher relative permittivity, the correct length for the material will leave the apparent impedance at the air-radome interface at P_4, where the impedance is completely real. In this way, the final horizontal movement to the left will leave the final impedance at the VSWR = 1 point. But this is essentially the same as making a single-layer radome that is 1/2 wavelength thick at the design frequency.

If a single-layer radome is 1/2 wavelength thick, the Smith chart is entered at a point. However, because a complete circling of the Smith chart is 1/2 wavelength, the chart is left from the same point at which it was entered. The end of the last chapter showed that this situation leads to a radome the transmission coefficient of which varies with frequency and angle of incidence. Figure 11.3 illustrates the equivalent case for the two-layer radome as the frequency of the wave varies.

Figure 11.4 shows a plot of the two-layer radome transmission as a function of frequency.

Let us return to the quarter-wave matching problem. The plate with a relative permittivity of 4.0, shown in Figure 11.5, is the three-layer radome.

The principle of quarter-wave matching for transmission lines lends itself almost directly to the radome transmission problem. As mentioned previously, the only difference is the changing of the wavelength in the media. Just as we choose the impedance of the quarter-wave matching line to be the geometric mean of the impedance of the lines to be matched, so can we choose the relative permittivity of the matching media to be the geometric mean of the permittivities of the materials to be matched. This selection gives us the parameters for the matching layers as

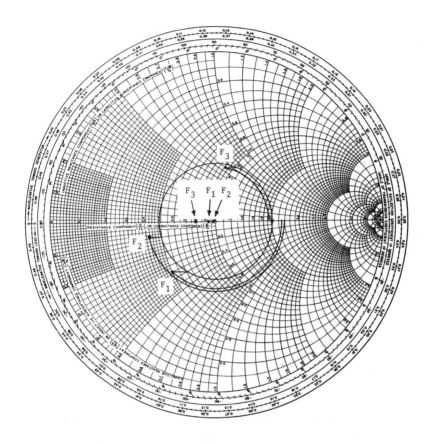

Fig. 11.3 Two-Layer Smith Chart with Variable Frequency

$$\text{Permittivity} = [(1)4]^{1/2} = 2.0$$
$$\text{Normal length} \qquad\quad = 0.53 \text{ cm}$$

Figure 11.6 presents the Smith chart for the three-layer quarter-wave matching problem.

We enter the Smith chart in Figure 11.6 at normalized impedance 1.414. Moving 1/4 wavelength around the Smith chart gives a normalized impedance at P_2 of 0.7071. If we wish to normalize the apparent impedance seen at interface #2 in Figure 11.6 to the impedance of the center layer, we scale the impedance at P_2 by the ratio of the impedances of the matching layer and the center layer, which in this case is 1.414. This change moves the total apparent impedance to 1.0.

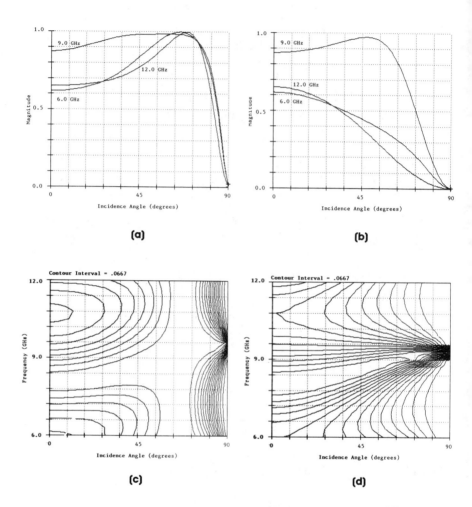

Fig. 11.4 Two-Layer Parallel and Perpendicular Transmission Coefficients

The matching operation has left the VSWR at 1.0. This means that the center layer can have an arbitrary length, and the total normalized impedance will not change. As will be seen when we consider frequency and angle of incidence dependency, we should keep the layer as thin as is practical because the path length in the medium is proportional to the normal length divided by the cosine of the transmission angle.

Once the center layer of Figure 11.5 has been crossed, the normalized impedance, which is still at 1.0, is normalized to the impedance of layer #1. It is easy to see that this normalization will take the impedance to P_1 on the

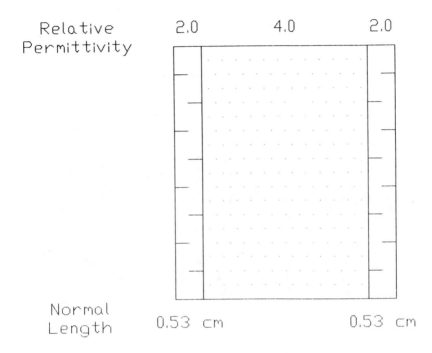

Relative Permittivity   2.0   4.0   2.0

Normal Length   0.53 cm   0.53 cm

Fig. 11.5 Three-Layer Quarter-Wave Matched Radome

Smith chart, and that circling the chart 1/4 wavelength will put the impedance back to P_2. Normalizing to the impedance of free space brings the VSWR back to 1.0.

As has been shown with the other radomes, the quarter-wave matched radome is a frequency-sensitive device. The single-layer radome will have maximum transmission when the thickness of the radome is 1/2 wavelength in the medium. For the frequency of interest (10 GHz) and a medium of $\epsilon_r = 4.0$, this thickness is 0.75 cm. Mechanically, this thickness may be too small. However, the layer can be any integer number of 1/2 wavelengths thick, so we let the material be 1 wavelength, 1.5 cm thick. Figure 11.7 illustrates the transmission characteristics as a function of the angle of incidence for this plate.

We have already calculated the required thickness and permittivity for the match plates. Figure 11.8 shows the transmission characteristics for the three-layer radome.

Three-layer matched radomes obviously offer a significant improvement over single-layer radomes. Figure 11.9 shows the transmission coefficients as a function of the off-boresight angle for a radome as described in Chapter 8. The radome shaping coefficient (*C*) is 2.0.

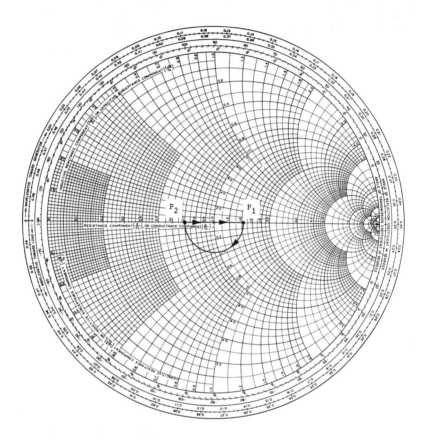

Fig. 11.6 Three-Layer Quarter-Wave Matched Smith Chart

If the phases of the transmission coefficients vary by more than a few tens of degrees, a potential for polarization rotations exists. Polarization rotations can be induced by differences in the magnitudes of the transmission coefficients; however, for matched three-layer radomes, the magnitudes of the transmission coefficients are not only usually close to 1, but tend to follow each other. Only at high angles of incidence do the magnitudes of the transmission coefficients differ significantly. Of course, polarization of the incoming signal plays a crucial role in determining whether a significant rotation of the transmitted wave will occur. If the incoming signal is polarized linearly and completely in either the parallel or perpendicular direction, there will be no rotation.

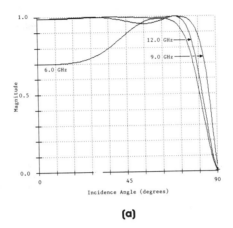

(a)

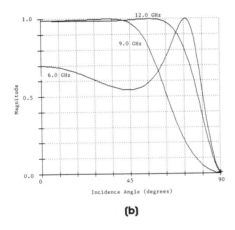

(b)

Fig. 11.7 Quarter-Wave Plate Parallel and Perpendicular Transmission Coefficients

    Circularly polarized signals also may or may not be rotated. If the wave is truly circularly polarized, the effect on the wave would be more like delaying the wave in time than rotating the polarization. This delay has the effect of distorting the beam shape of the antenna that the radome houses. Thus, while three-layer radomes are an improvement over single-layer radomes in terms of the magnitude of the transmission coefficient, five-layer radomes are an improvement in terms of the phase of the transmission coefficient.

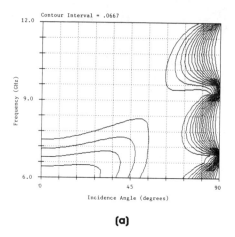

(a)

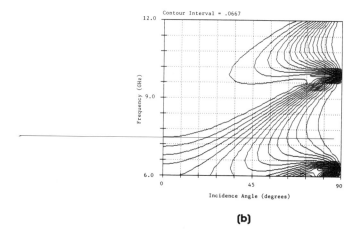

(b)

Fig. 11.8 Three-Layer Parallel and Perpendicular Transmission Coefficients

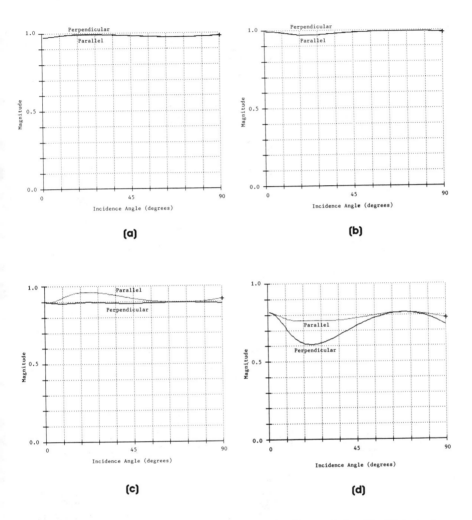

Fig. 11.9 Three-Layer Parallel and Perpendicular Transmission Coefficients Including Radome Shape Function

11.3 ANTISTATIC LAYERS

But before moving on to five-layer radomes, we should mention what may be considered four-layer radomes. The case of the two-layer radome showed that having an even number of layers does not offer some of the advantages that may be obtained with a three-layer (odd-numbered) configuration. Most radomes used today are not truly symmetric, either due to an antistatic layer or an erosion-resistant layer. These layers are usually relatively thin and typically have high permittivities. Figure 11.10 presents transmission data for the three-layer matched radome with an antistatic layer of relative permittivity 7.0 and thickness 0.1 cm.

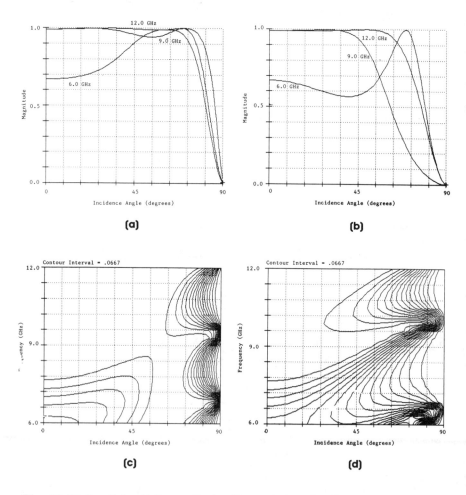

Fig. 11.10 Parallel and Perpendicular Transmission Coefficients for a Three-Layer Radome with an Antistatic Layer

It is clear that an antistatic layer can seriously degrade radome performance. At normal incidence for the three-layer matched radome, having an antistatic layer is equivalent to putting a thin radome with a high permittivity in front of an antenna that had no radome. It is interesting to note that as the layer becomes vanishingly small, only the magnitudes of the transmission coefficients change.

If the permittivity of the "odd layer out" is less than that of the outermost matched radome layer, then the effects are not too severe.

11.4 FIVE-LAYER RADOMES

We can extend the quarter-wave matching principle to include more layers simply by matching the outermost layer to air with yet another layer. In the previous example, where the matching layer had a relative permittivity of 2.0, we found the required permittivity by taking the geometric mean of the two media permittivities. Continuing this procedure gives the necessary permittivities for the two new layers as $2^{1/2}$. Once again, the phase length in the media must be equal to 1/4 wavelength. This length is 0.63 cm. Notice that the ray path through the five-layer radome in Figure 11.11 gets progressively shallower going into the radome.

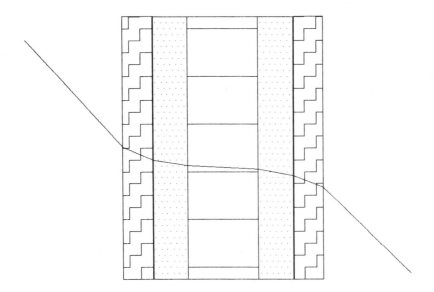

Fig. 11.11 Five-Layer Quarter-Wave Matched Radome

The layers in Figure 11.11 are drawn to scale. As the permittivities decrease away from the center layer, the normal lengths of the layers must increase in order to stay at 1/4 wavelength for the design frequency. Only the center layer has an arbitrary length. In the current example, the radome is 2.82 cm thick. Figure 11.12 supplies transmission coefficient data for the five-layer radome as a function of angle of incidence.

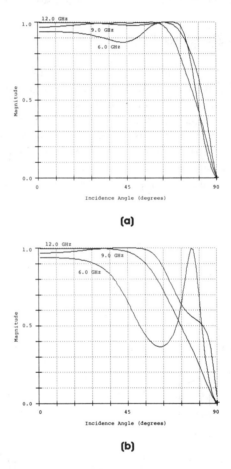

Fig. 11.12 Five-Layer Parallel and Perpendicular Transmission Coefficients

Data for transmission coefficients as a function of angle of incidence and frequency are shown in Figure 11.13.

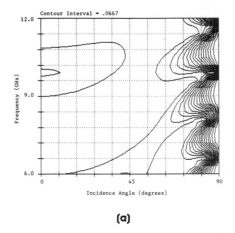

(a)

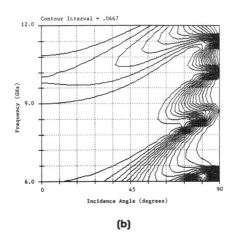

(b)

Fig. 11.13 Five-Layer Parallel and Perpendicular Transmission Coefficients as a Function of Frequency

The bandwith of the five-layer radome is, as expected, better than either the single-layer or three-layer radome. The phase response is particularly improved.

Figure 11.14 shows the difference in phase between the transmission coefficients. We can easily see that the five-layer radome imparts less polarization distortion on the waves passing through it than would a three-layer radome.

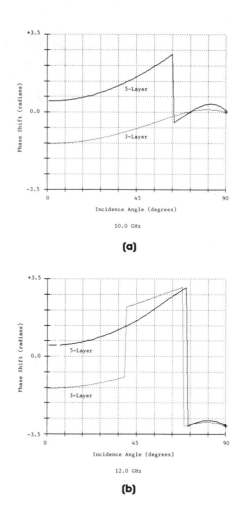

Fig. 11.14 Five-Layer Relative Phase Shift Characteristic

11.5 SUMMARY

Multilayered radomes are ideal to use because they possess superior transmission characteristics, both in magnitude and phase.

We established the utility of the radome model through the several multilayered radome examples. The model offers the means to apply Smith chart techniques to the problem of radome transmission in an efficient and convenient manner.

Before closing, we should review the entire radome modeling technique. This technique makes two significant simplifying assumptions:

1. A single-ray transmission calculation for a planar surface may represent the effect of the projection of the antenna aperture on the curved surface of the radome.
2. The radome may be considered lossless.

We still must answer an important question: how legitimate are these assumptions? The answer is a function of the intended use of the model.

For the proper physical constants and shape of a given radome, this modeling technique will not give a precisely correct transmission. However, the trend of the transmission function as a function of incidence angle will closely replicate that of the actual radome. In addition, by taking some artistic license with the permittivities and thicknesses of the layers, the creative modeler can achieve a very good fit to a given radome without the computational overhead of a rigorous solution, which would account for lossy materials and integrated effects over a surface area.

Appendix A
Antenna Simulation Models

A.1 ANTENNA ALGORITHM MODELS

The following programs and subroutines represent software implementations of the antenna simulation algorithms and functions described in Part II. The routines are written in BASIC and, in all cases, are referenced to appropriate sections of the text, in which they were derived or explained.

Following the listings, we present an example antenna simulation using the programs and subroutines listed. This example demonstrates how the software is used to create a desired antenna pattern.

```
1000 REM ***********************************************************
1001 REM *                                                         *
1002 REM *   SUBROUTINE VOLTGN (VOLTAGE GAIN)                      *
1003 REM *                                                         *
1004 REM *   INPUTS: TH = COMPOSITE ANGLE (RADIANS)                *
1005 REM *           L = LOWER ANGULAR BOUNDARY (RADIANS)          *
1006 REM *           U = UPPER ANGULAR BOUNDARY (RADIANS)          *
1007 REM *           M = MAXIMUM RELATIVE LOBE GAIN (dBVG)         *
1008 REM *           E = SHAPING COEFFICIENT                       *
1009 REM *           N = LOBE NUMBER                               *
1010 REM *                                                         *
1011 REM *   OUTPUTS: DBVG = RELATIVE dB VOLTAGE GAIN             *
1012 REM *            VG = ACTUAL RELATIVE VOLTAGE GAIN           *
```

```
1013 REM *                 SL = LOBE SIGN COEFFICIENT (+ or -) *
1014 REM *                                                     *
1015 REM *  REFERENCE: TEXT SECTIONS 3.1, 4.1                  *
1016 REM *                                                     *
1019 REM ****************************************************
1020 LET PI = 3.141592654#
1025 LET TEM = SIN((TH-L)*PI/(U-L))
1030 IF TEM<0 THEN LET TEM=0
1035 LET DBVG = ((TEM^E)*(100+M))-100
1040 LET VG = 10^(DBVG/10)
1045 IF N/2 = INT(N/2) THEN LET SL = -1 ELSE LET SL = 1
1050 RETURN
1100 REM ****************************************************
1101 REM *                                                  *
1102 REM *  SUBROUTINE TRISHP (TRIANGULAR SHAPING)          *
1103 REM *                                                  *
1104 REM *  INPUTS: TH = COMPOSITE ANGLE (RADIANS)          *
1105 REM *          W = WEIGHTING RELATIVE TO VOLTAGE        *
1106 REM *              GAIN FUNCTION                        *
1107 REM *          L = LOWER ANGULAR BOUNDARY (RADIANS)     *
1108 REM *          U = UPPER ANGULAR BOUNDARY (RADIANS)     *
1109 REM *          VG = ACTUAL RELATIVE VOLTAGE GAIN        *
1110 REM *          M = MAXIMUM RELATIVE LOBE GAIN (dBVG)    *
1111 REM *                                                  *
1112 REM *  OUTPUTS: VG = ACTUAL RELATIVE VOLTAGE GAIN,     *
1113 REM *               AFTER SHAPING                       *
1114 REM *          DBVG = dB VOLTAGE GAIN, AFTER SHAPING    *
1115 REM *               (dBVG)                              *
```

```
1116 REM *                                                    *
1117 REM *   REFERENCE: TEXT SECTION 4.2                       *
1118 REM *                                                    *
1119 REM ****************************************************
1120 LET CEN = L+(U-L)/2
1125 LET B = W*(10^(M/10))
1130 LET SLOPE = -2*B/(U-L)
1135 LET ST = SLOPE*ABS(CEN-TH)+B
1140 LET VG = (ST+VG)/(W+1)
1145 LET DBVG = 10*(LOG(ABS(VG))/LOG(10))
1150 RETURN
1200 REM ****************************************************
1201 REM *                                                    *
1202 REM *   SUBROUTINE ANGDIS (ANGULAR DISTORTION)           *
1203 REM *                                                    *
1204 REM *   INPUTS: TA = AZIMUTH ANGLE (RADIANS)             *
1205 REM *           TE = ELEVATION ANGLE (RADIANS)           *
1206 REM *           DA = AZIMUTH DISTORTION COEFFICIENT       *
1207 REM *                (PERCENT)                           *
1208 REM *           DE = ELEVATION DISTORTION COEFFICIENT     *
1209 REM *                (PERCENT)                           *
1210 REM *                                                    *
1211 REM *   OUTPUTS: TA = MODIFIED AZIMUTH ANGLE (RADIANS) *
1213 REM *            TE = MODIFIED ELEVATION ANGLE          *
1214 REM *                 (RADIANS)                         *
1215 REM *                                                    *
1216 REM *   REFERENCE: TEXT SECTION 4.3                      *
1217 REM *                                                    *
```

```
1218 REM ****************************************************
1220 LET TA = TA*(100/DA)
1225 LET TE = TE*(100/DE)
1230 RETURN
1400 REM ****************************************************
1401 REM *                                                  *
1402 REM *   SUBROUTINE COMANG (COMPOSITE ANGLE)            *
1403 REM *                                                  *
1404 REM *   INPUTS: TA = AZIMUTH ANGLE (RADIANS)           *
1405 REM *           TE = ELEVATION ANGLE (RADIANS)         *
1406 REM *                                                  *
1407 REM *   OUTPUT: TH = COMPOSITE ANGLE (RADIANS)         *
1408 REM *                                                  *
1409 REM ****************************************************
1410 LET PI = 3.141592654#
1420 LET NUM = (1 -(COS(TA)*COS(TE))^2)^.5
1425 LET DEN = COS(TA)*COS(TE)
1430 LET TNG = ABS(NUM/DEN)
1435 LET TH = ATN(TNG)
1440 IF ABS(TE)>PI/2 THEN GOTO 1455
1445 IF ABS(TA)>PI/2 THEN GOTO 1455
1450 GOTO 1460
1455 LET TH = PI - TH
1460 RETURN
1500 REM ****************************************************
1501 REM *                                                  *
1502 REM *   SUBROUTINE ROTANG (ROTATIONAL ANGLE)           *
1503 REM *                                                  *
```

```
1504 REM *   INPUTS: TA = AZIMUTH ANGLE (RADIANS)          *
1505 REM *           TE = ELEVATION ANGLE (RADIANS)        *
1506 REM *                                                 *
1507 REM *   OUTPUTS: PH = ROTATIONAL ANGLE (RADIANS)      *
1508 REM *                                                 *
1509 REM    REFERENCE: TEXT SECTION 4.4                    *
1510 REM *                                                 *
1511 REM ****************************************************
1520 IF TE = Ø THEN LET TE = 1E-1Ø
1525 IF TA = Ø THEN LET TA = 1E-1Ø
1530 LET TNN = ABS(SIN(TA)/SIN(TE))
1535 LET PH = ATN(TNN)
1540 IF TA<Ø AND TE>Ø THEN LET PH = 2*PI - PH
1545 IF TA<Ø AND TE<Ø THEN LET PH = PI + PH
1555 IF TA>Ø AND TE<Ø THEN LET PH = PI - PH
1560 RETURN
1600 REM ****************************************************
1601 REM *                                                 *
1602 REM *   SUBROUTINE RADMOD (RADIAL MODULATION)         *
1603 REM *                                                 *
1604 REM *   INPUTS: NC = NUMBER OF CYCLES                 *
1605 REM *           FP = POLARITY FLAG                    *
1606 REM *           PM = MODULATION PERCENTAGE            *
1607 REM *           CC = NULL CYCLE COUNT                 *
1608 REM *                (NUMBER OF NULL CYCLES)          *
1609 REM *        NLC(CC) = NULL CYCLE NUMBERS             *
1610 REM *                                                 *
1611 REM *   OUTPUT: RM = RADIAL MODULATION COEFFICIENT    *
```

```
1612 REM *                                                        *
1613 REM *   REFERENCE: TEXT SECTION 4.4                          *
1614 REM *                                                        *
1615 REM ************************************************************
1620 LET PI = 3.141592654#
1621 LET CSF = COS(NC*PH+PI*FP)
1622 LET CSGN = 1
1623 IF CSF < 0 THEN LET CSGN = -1
1624 LET CSFN = ((ABS(CSF))^.5)*CSGN
1625 LET RM = .5 + CSFN/2
1630 IF RM<0 THEN LET RM = 0
1632 LET RM = (RM*PM+100-PM)/100
1635 LET H = INT((NC*PH+PI*FP)/(2*PI)+.5)
1636 IF H = 0 THEN LET H =NC
1640 FOR J = 1 TO CC
1645 IF H = NLC(J) THEN LET RM = (100-PM)/100
1646 IF RM<0 THEN LET RM = 0
1650 NEXT J
1655 RETURN
1700 REM ************************************************************
1701 REM *                                                        *
1702 REM *   SUBROUTINE POINT (ELECTRONIC POINTING)               *
1703 REM *                                                        *
1704 REM *   INPUTS:    PA = AZIMUTH POINTING ANGLE               *
1705 REM *             PE = ELEVATION POINTING ANGLE              *
1706 REM *             TA = AZIMUTH ANGLE                         *
1707 REM *             TE = ELEVATION ANGLE                       *
1710 REM *                                                        *
```

```
1711 REM *   OUTPUTS:    TA = MODIFIED AZIMUTH ANGLE          *

1712 REM *               TE = MODIFIED ELEVATION ANGLE        *

1713 REM *                                                    *

1714 REM *   NOTE:       ALL ANGLES IN RADIANS               *

1715 REM *                                                    *

1716 REM *   REFERENCE: TEXT SECTION 6.2                      *

1718 REM *                                                    *

1719 REM *****************************************************

1720 LET PI = 3.141592654#

1725 IF PA = Ø THEN GOTO 1727

1726 GOTO 1730

1727 IF PE = Ø THEN GOTO 1760

1730 LET SNTE = SIN(PE + TE) - SIN(PE)

1735 LET TE = ATN(SNTE/((1 - (SNTE)^2)^.5))

1740 LET FCN1 = SIN(PA + TA)*COS(PE + TE)

1745 LET FCN2 = SIN(PA)*COS(PE)

1750 LET SNTA = (FCN1-FCN2)/COS(TE)

1755 LET TA = ATN(SNTA/((1 - (SNTA)^2)^.5))

1760 RETURN

1800 REM *****************************************************

1801 REM *                                                    *

1802 REM *   SUBROUTINE PNTLOS (POINTING LOSS)               *

1803 REM *                                                    *

1804 REM *   INPUTS: BW = UNSTEERED BEAMWIDTH                *

1805 REM *           PE = ELEVATION POINTING ANGLE           *

1806 REM *           PA = AZIMUTH POINTING ANGLE             *

1807 REM *                                                    *

1808 REM *   OUTPUTS: GS = THE TOTAL LOSS COEFFICIENT        *
```

```
1809 REM *                  DUE TO POINTING (STEERING)        *

1810 REM *                                                    *

1811 REM *  NOTE: ALL ANGLES ARE IN RADIANS                   *

1812 REM *                                                    *

1813 REM *  REFERENCE: TEXT SECTION 6.1                       *

1818 REM *                                                    *

1819 REM ****************************************************

1820 REM

1821 REM    CALCULATE APERTURE COEFFICIENT

1822 REM

1830 LET GSA = (COS(PE)*COS(PA))^.5

1832 REM

1834 REM    CALCULATE INCREASED BEAMWIDTH COEFFICIENT

1836 REM

1840 LET BWH = BW/2

1842 GOSUB 1880

1844 LET TPSE = TSE

1846 LET TPSA = TSA

1850 LET BWH = -1*BW/2

1852 GOSUB 1880

1854 LET TNSE = TSE

1856 LET TNSA = TSA

1860 LET GSB = BW/(((TPSA-TNSA)*(TPSE-TNSE))^.5)

1862 LET GVS = GSA*GSB

1864 RETURN

1874 REM    ***** UTILITY SUBROUTINE ******

1876 REM

1878 REM    STEERED HALF-ANGLE CALCULATIONS
```

```
1880 REM

1882 LET SNF1 = SIN(BWH) + SIN(PE)

1884 LET TSE = ATN(SNF1/((1-SNF1^2)^.5)) - PE

1886 LET SNUM = SIN(BWH)*COS(BWH) + SIN(PA)*COS(PE)

1888 LET SNF2 = SNUM/COS(PE+TSE)

1890 LET TSA = ATN(SNF2/((1-SNF2^2)^.5)) - PA

1892 RETURN

1 REM   ****************************************************

2 REM   *                                                *

3 REM   *     PROGRAM PKGAIN:                            *

4 REM   *                                                *

5 REM   *     CALCULATES AZIMUTH AND ELEVATION HALF-POWER *

6 REM   *     BEAMWIDTH, AND PEAK POWER AND VOLTAGE GAINS *

7 REM   *     AS A FUNCTION OF VOLTAGE GAIN MODEL INPUT  *

8 REM   *     COEFFICIENTS.                              *

9 REM   *                                                *

10 REM  *     REFERENCE: TEXT SECTION 4.2               *

11 REM  *                                                *

12 REM  ****************************************************

15 CLS

17 DIM INC(3)

20 INPUT "LOWER ANGULAR BOUNDARY (DEGREES)"; THTALO

25 INPUT "UPPER ANGULAR BOUNDARY (DEGREES)"; THTAHI

30 INPUT "MAXIMUM dBvg"; MXDBVG

35 INPUT "EXPONENTIAL SHAPING COEFFICIENT"; EXPSHP

40 INPUT "TRIANGULAR WEIGHTING COEFFICIENT"; TRIWGT

45 INPUT "AZIMUTH DISTORTION (PERCENT)"; DISTAZ

50 INPUT "ELEVATION DISTORTION (PERCENT)"; DISTEL
```

```
85 LET MAXVGN = 10^(MXDBVG/10)

90 LET PI = 3.141592654#

95 LET DEGRAD = PI/180

105 LET INC(1) = 1

110 LET INC(2) = .1

115 LET INC(3) = .01

120 LET INDEX = 1

125 LET CNT = 01

130 LET CNT = CNT + INC(INDEX)

140 LET WTERM = TRIWGT*MAXVGN*(((-1*CNT)/(((THTAHI-
    THTALO)/2)) + 11)

145 LET STERM = (SIN(((CNT-THTALO)/(THTAHI-THTALO))*PI))

150 LET STERM = (STERM^EXPSHP)*(MXDBVG+100)-100

151 LET STERM = 10^(STERM/10)

153 LET FUNC = (WTERM + STERM)/(TRIWGT + 1)

155 LET GFUNC = 10*(LOG(FUNC))/(LOG(10))

160 IF GFUNC > (MXDBVG - 1.5) THEN GOTO 130

165 LET CNT = CNT - INC(INDEX)

170 LET INDEX = INDEX + 1

175 IF INDEX = 4 THEN GOTO 185

180 GOTO 140

185 LET THTA = 2*CNT

190 PRINT

195 PRINT "BASIC FUNCTION BEAMWIDTH:     ";THTA;"DEGREES ,";

200 PRINT THTA*DEGRAD;"RADIANS"

205 PRINT

210 LET AZBW = THTA*DISTAZ/100

215 LET AZBWR = AZBW*DEGRAD
```

```
220 LET ELBW = THTA*DISTEL/100
225 LET ELBWR = ELBW*DEGRAD
230 PRINT "AZIMUTH BEAMWIDTH:          ";AZBW;"DEGREES ,";
235 PRINT AZBWR;"RADIANS"
240 PRINT
245 PRINT "ELEVATION BEAMWIDTH:        ";ELBW;"DEGREES ,";
250 PRINT ELBWR;"RADIANS"
255 PRINT
260 LET GPOWER = 4*PI/(AZBWR*ELBWR)
265 LET APOWER = 10*(LOG(GPOWER))/(LOG(10))
270 LET GVOLTS = GPOWER^.5
275 LET AVOLTS = 10*(LOG(GVOLTS))/(LOG(10))
280 PRINT "PEAK POWER GAIN:       ";GPOWER;",  ";APOWER;"dB"
285 PRINT
290 PRINT "PEAK VOLTAGE GAIN:     ";GVOLTS;",  ";AVOLTS;"dBvg"
300 PRINT
305 INPUT "TYPE 'R' TO REPEAT, ELSE EXIT";A$
310 CLS
315 IF A$ = "R" THEN GOTO 20
320 END
```

A.2 INPUT-OUTPUT UTILITIES AND DRIVER

The following programs allow the user to enter and modify the parameters required for the antenna simulation subroutines and to display the gain pattern through a simple BASIC graphics utility. The driver provides a means for calling the input-output utilities and the previously listed simulation subroutines in the sequence described in Part II of the text, thus creating a useful and interactive means for producing and assessing gain patterns.

The graphics utility is quite machine-dependent. This utility is useful in applications where a more versatile, file-based graphics system is not available.

However, the graphics system is recommended for extensive analysis applications. The user should be able to replace the calls to the graphics utility with file management commands and create data files compatible with whatever graphics system is available.

```
6100 REM **************************************************
6101 REM *                                                *
6102 REM *   SUBROUTINE SETUP (ENTER PARAMETERS)          *
6109 REM *                                                *
6110 REM **************************************************
6115 CLS
6120 PRINT
6125 PRINT "ENTER DATA IN RESPONSE TO QUERIES."
6130 PRINT
6135 INPUT "ENTER NUMBER OF LOBES (<=4)";NL
6140 IF NL > 4 THEN GOTO 135
6144 REM
6145 REM ***** DIMENSION SELECTED VARIABLES *****
6146 REM
6147 DIM L(NL)
6148 DIM U(NL)
6149 DIM M(NL)
6150 DIM E(NL)
6151 DIM W(NL)
6152 DIM NC(NL)
6153 DIM FP(NL)
6154 DIM PM(NL)
6155 DIM CC(NL)
6156 DIM NLCC(NL,16)
6157 DIM NLC(16)
```

```
6158 CLS

6159 PRINT

6160 PRINT "***** ENTERING DATA FOR";NL;"LOBE(S). *****"

6162 LET DTR = 3.141592654#/180

6165 FOR I = 1 TO NL

6166 PRINT

6170 PRINT "FOR LOBE #";I;"ENTER:"

6175 IF I = 1 THEN INPUT "LOWER ANGULAR BOUNDARY
     (DEGREES)";LL ELSE LET LL = U(I-1)/DTR

6176 LET L(I) = LL*DTR

6180 INPUT "UPPER ANGULAR BOUNDARY (DEGREES)";UU

6181 LET U(I) = UU*DTR

6182 INPUT "MAXIMUM RELATIVE VOLTAGE GAIN (dBVG)";M(I)

6183 INPUT "SHAPING COEFFICIENT (DIMENSIONLESS)";E(I)

6184 INPUT "TRIANGULAR SHAPE WEIGHTING";W(I)

6185 INPUT "NUMBER OF RADIAL MODULATION (RM) CYCLES";NC(I)

6186 IF NC(I) = 0 THEN GOTO 6200

6187 INPUT "POLARITY FLAG (RM)";FP(I)

6188 INPUT "MODULATION PERCENTAGE (0 to 100)";PM(I)

6189 INPUT "NUMBER OF NULL CYCLES (RM)(<=16)";CC(I)

6190 FOR J = 1 TO CC(I)

6191 INPUT "NULL CYCLE NUMBER";NLCC(I,J)

6192 NEXT J

6200 NEXT I

6201 CLS

6205 PRINT

6206 PRINT "***** SETTING UP ANGULAR DISTORTION *****"

6207 PRINT
```

```
6210 INPUT "AZIMUTH DISTORTION COEFFICIENT (PER CENT)";DA
6215 INPUT "ELEVATION DISTORTION COEFFICIENT (PER CENT)";DE
6218 CLS
6220 PRINT
6222 PRINT "*** SETTING UP PLANAR ARRAY POINTING ANGLES ***"
6224 PRINT "        (ENTER Øs IF NOT PLANAR ARRAY)"
6226 PRINT
6228 INPUT "AZIMUTH POINTING ANGLE";PA
6229 LET PA = PA*DTR
6230 INPUT "ELEVATION POINTING ANGLE";PE
6231 LET PE = PE*DTR
6280 RETURN
7000 REM ***************************************************
7001 REM *                                                 *
7002 REM *   SUBROUTINE MODIFY (CHANGE SETUP PARAMETERS)   *
7003 REM *                                                 *
7004 REM ***************************************************
7012 CLS
7015 PRINT "PRESENT SETUP IS:
7016 PRINT
7018 FOR I = 1 TO NL
7020 PRINT "   "I,
7021 NEXT I
7022 PRINT "  (N)
7027 FOR I = 1 TO NL
7028 PRINT " -------",
7029 NEXT I
7030 PRINT " ----"
```

```
7033 FOR I = 1 TO NL
7035 PRINT L(I)/DTR,
7036 NEXT I
7037 PRINT " L(N)
7038 FOR I = 1 TO NL
7040 PRINT U(I)/DTR,
7041 NEXT I
7042 PRINT " U(N)
7043 FOR I = 1 TO NL
7045 PRINT M(I),
7046 NEXT I
7047 PRINT " M(N)
7048 FOR I = 1 TO NL
7050 PRINT E(I),
7051 NEXT I
7052 PRINT " E(N)
7053 FOR I = 1 TO NL
7055 PRINT W(I),
7056 NEXT I
7057 PRINT " W(N)
7061 FOR I = 1 TO NL
7062 PRINT NC(I),
7063 NEXT I
7064 PRINT " NC(N)
7065 FOR I = 1 TO NL
7066 PRINT FP(I),
7067 NEXT I
7068 PRINT " FP(N)
```

```
7069 FOR I = 1 TO NL

7070 PRINT PM(I),

7071 NEXT I

7072 PRINT " PM(N)

7075 FOR I = 1 TO NL

7076 PRINT CC(I),

7077 NEXT I

7078 PRINT " CC(N)

7080 LET CCMAX = CC(1)

7081 FOR I = 2 TO NL

7083 IF CC(I) > CC(I-1) THEN LET CCMAX = CC(I)

7085 NEXT I

7087 FOR J = 1 TO CCMAX

7089 FOR I = 1 TO NL

7091 IF J > CC(I) THEN PRINT "--", ELSE PRINT NLCC(I,J),

7093 NEXT I

7095 PRINT " NLC(N,";J;")"

7097 NEXT J

7100 PRINT

7101 INPUT "WANT TO MODIFY [VARIABLE] OR CONTINUE [C]";MD$

7105 IF MD$ = "C" THEN GOTO 7200

7110 IF MD$ = "L(1)" THEN INPUT L(1) : LET L(1) = L(1)*DTR

7111 IF MD$ = "L(2)" THEN INPUT L(2) : LET L(2) = L(2)*DTR

7112 IF MD$ = "L(3)" THEN INPUT L(3) : LET L(3) = L(3)*DTR

7113 IF MD$ = "L(4)" THEN INPUT L(4) : LET L(4) = L(4)*DTR

7114 IF MD$ = "U(1)" THEN INPUT U(1) : LET U(1) = U(1)*DTR

7115 IF MD$ = "U(2)" THEN INPUT U(2) : LET U(2) = U(2)*DTR

7116 IF MD$ = "U(3)" THEN INPUT U(3) : LET U(3) = U(3)*DTR
```

```
7117 IF MD$ = "U(4)" THEN INPUT U(4) : LET U(4) = U(4)*DTR
7118 IF MD$ = "M(1)" THEN INPUT M(1)
7119 IF MD$ = "M(2)" THEN INPUT M(2)
7120 IF MD$ = "M(3)" THEN INPUT M(3)
7121 IF MD$ = "M(4)" THEN INPUT M(4)
7122 IF MD$ = "E(1)" THEN INPUT E(1)
7123 IF MD$ = "E(2)" THEN INPUT E(2)
7124 IF MD$ = "E(3)" THEN INPUT E(3)
7125 IF MD$ = "E(4)" THEN INPUT E(4)
7126 IF MD$ = "W(1)" THEN INPUT W(1)
7127 IF MD$ = "W(2)" THEN INPUT W(2)
7128 IF MD$ = "W(3)" THEN INPUT W(3)
7129 IF MD$ = "W(4)" THEN INPUT W(4)
7130 IF MD$ = "NC(1)" THEN INPUT NC(1)
7131 IF MD$ = "NC(2)" THEN INPUT NC(2)
7132 IF MD$ = "NC(3)" THEN INPUT NC(3)
7133 IF MD$ = "NC(4)" THEN INPUT NC(4)
7134 IF MD$ = "FP(1)" THEN INPUT FP(1)
7135 IF MD$ = "FP(2)" THEN INPUT FP(2)
7136 IF MD$ = "FP(3)" THEN INPUT FP(3)
7137 IF MD$ = "FP(4)" THEN INPUT FP(4)
7140 IF MD$ = "PM(1)" THEN INPUT PM(1)
7141 IF MD$ = "PM(2)" THEN INPUT PM(2)
7142 IF MD$ = "PM(3)" THEN INPUT PM(3)
7143 IF MD$ = "PM(4)" THEN INPUT PM(4)
7199 GOTO 7012
7200 CLS
7205 PRINT "PRESENT SETUP IS:"
```

```
7211 PRINT
7214 PRINT "DA =";DA,,"DE =";DE
7215 PRINT
7216 PRINT "PA =";PA/DTR,,"PE =";PE/DTR
7220 PRINT
7222 INPUT "WANT TO MODIFY [VARIABLE] OR CONTINUE [C]";MD$
7224 IF MD$ = "C" THEN RETURN
7226 IF MD$ = "PA" THEN INPUT PA : LET PA = PA*DTR
7228 IF MD$ = "PE" THEN INPUT PE : LET PE = PE*DTR
7230 IF MD$ = "DA" THEN INPUT DA
7232 IF MD$ = "DE" THEN INPUT DE
7250 GOTO 7200
5000 REM ****************************************************
5001 REM *                                                  *
5002 REM *   SUBROUTINE GNPLOT (GAIN PLOT)                  *
5003 REM *                                                  *
5004 REM *   INPUTS: FP = PLOT FLAG (0 = dB, 1 = DBVG,      *
5005 REM *                  2 = VG, 3 = PG)                 *
5006 REM *       GD(151) = ARRAY OF GAIN DATA, DIMENSIONED  *
5007 REM *                 FROM 1 TO 60.  ALLOWABLE RANGES: *
5008 REM *                   0 TO -50 (dB OR dBVG)          *
5009 REM *                   0 TO 1.0 (VG OR PG)            *
5010 REM *                                                  *
5011 REM *   OUTPUTS: PLOT OF GAIN AS A FUNCTION OF ANGLE   *
5012 REM *                                                  *
5013 REM *   NOTE:  THIS PLOTTING UTILITY IS DESIGNED FOR   *
5014 REM *          A "HERCULES" GRAPHICS SYSTEM OPERATING  *
5015 REM *          IN HIGH RESOLUTION MONOCHROME MODE.     *
```

```
5016 REM *            MODIFICATIONS MAY BE REQUIRED TO MAKE    *
5017 REM *            IT FUNCTIONAL ON OTHER SYSTEMS.          *
5018 REM *                                                     *
5020 REM ********************************************************
5110 CLS
5115 SCREEN 3,0,0,0
5120 FOR I= 0 TO 10
5122 IF  I = 0 THEN LINE ((177+48*I),16)-((177+48*I),260)
5125 LINE ((177+48*I),17)-((177+48*I),260),,,&H1
5130 NEXT I
5135 FOR I = 0 TO 5
5140 LET P = 16 + 48*I
5142 IF I = 5 THEN LINE (172,P)-(656,P)
5145 LINE (176,P)-(656,P),,,&H1
5150 NEXT I
5155 LOCATE 20,19,0,0,0
5160 PRINT "-15                    0                    +15"
5165 LOCATE 22,40,0,0,0
5170 PRINT "THETA (DEGREES)
5175 FOR I = 0 TO 1
5180 LOCATE 2+17*I,15,0,0,0
5185 IF FP > 1 THEN PRINT 1 -1.25*I ELSE PRINT I*-50
5190 NEXT I
5195 LOCATE 10,13,0,0,0
5200 IF FP < 2 THEN PRINT "dB"
5205 LOCATE 11,13,0,0,0
5210 IF FP > 0 THEN IF FP < 3 THEN PRINT "VG" ELSE PRINT
     "PG"
```

```
5220 IF FP > 1 THEN LET SC = 192 ELSE LET SC = 192/40
5225 IF FP > 1 THEN LET SR = 208 ELSE LET SR = 16
5226 LET SP = SR - SC*GD(0)
5227 IF SP > 256 THEN LET SP = 256
5230 PSET (177,SP)
5235 FOR I = 1 TO 60
5236 LET EP = SR - SC*GD(I)
5237 IF EP > 256 THEN LET EP = 256
5240 LINE - (177 + I*81,EP)
5245 NEXT I
5250 LOCATE 23,1,0,0,0
5255 RETURN
10 REM ***************************************************
12 REM *                                                 *
14 REM *   ANTENNA SIMULATION DRIVER                     *
16 REM *                                                 *
20 REM ***************************************************
24 REM
25 REM *****   SET UP GAIN MODEL PARAMETERS, CONSTANTS ******
26 REM
27 DIM GAIN(3600)
30 DIM HG(4)
33 DIM GD(61)
34 GOSUB 6100:REM              ****** SETUP PARAMETERS ******
35 GOSUB 7000:REM              ****** MODIFY PARAMETERS ******
40 LET PI = 3.141592654#
45 LET DTR = PI/180
49 REM
```

```
50 REM ******   SELECT MONOPULSE OR SINGLE ANTENNA   ********

51 REM

55 CLS

114 PRINT

115 INPUT "ENTER ELEVATION OFFSET ANGLE, (degrees)";TC

125 FOR I = 1 TO 60

127 LET TE = TC*DTR

130 LET TA = (-15 + I*.5)*DTR

135 GOSUB 1200:REM              ***** ANGULAR DISTORTION ******

140 GOSUB 1700:REM              ***** ELECTRONIC POINTING *****

145 GOSUB 1400:REM              ****** COMPOSITE ANGLE *******

150 GOSUB 1500:REM              ****** ROTATIONAL ANGLE *******

155 IF ABS(TH) <= U(NL) THEN GOTO 170

160 LET VG = 1E-10

165 GOTO 250

170 FOR J = 1 TO NL

175 IF L(J) < TH THEN IF TH <= U(J) THEN LET LB = J

180 NEXT J

185 LET L = -1*E10

190 LET L = L(LB)

195 LET U = U(LB)

200 LET M = M(LB)

205 LET E = E(LB)

60 INPUT "ENTER [M] FOR MONOPULSE, [S] FOR SINGLE
   ANTENNA;";TYPE$

64 REM

65 REM *************** SET UP FILE SIZE *****************

66 REM
```

```
68 PRINT
69 PRINT "SELECT 3-D (MATRIX) OR 2-D (SLICE):"
70 INPUT "ENTER [M] FOR MATRIX, [S] FOR SLICE";FILE$
75 IF FILE$ = "M" THEN LET SIZE = 3600 ELSE LET SIZE = 60
79 REM
80 REM ****** BRANCH TO SINGLE OR MONOPULSE PROCESS ******
81 REM
85 IF TYPE$ = "M" THEN GOTO 300
89 REM
90 REM ********** BEGIN SINGLE ANTENNA PROCESS ***********
91 REM
95 LET ACC = 0
100 IF FILE$ = "S" THEN GOTO 114 ELSE FOR K = 1 TO 60
105 LET TC = (-15 +K*.5)
110 GOTO 125
210 LET N = LB
215 GOSUB 1000:REM           ********* VOLTAGE GAIN *********
220 LET W = W(LB)
225 GOSUB 1100:REM           ****** TRIANGULAR SHAPING ******
230 LET NC = NC(LB)
235 LET FP = FP(LB)
240 LET PM = PM(LB)
245 LET CC = CC(LB)
250 FOR J = 1 TO CC
255 LET NLC(J) = NLCC(LB,J)
260 NEXT J
265 GOSUB 1600:REM           ****** RADIAL MODULATION ******
270 LET VG = VG*RM*SL
```

```
275 LET ACC = ACC +1
280 IF VG = Ø THEN LET GAIN(ACC) = 1E-1Ø ELSE LET GAIN(ACC)=
    VG
282 PRINT TC,(I/2)-15,GAIN(ACC)
285 NEXT I
290 IF FILE$ = "M" THEN NEXT K
295 GOTO 5ØØ
299 REM
3ØØ REM ***** BEGIN MONOPULSE PROCESS *****
3Ø2 REM
3Ø4 CLS
3Ø6 PRINT "MONOPULSE PROCESSING"
3Ø8 PRINT
31Ø INPUT "ENTER AZIMUTH SQUINT ANGLE (degrees)";SQAZ
312 INPUT "ENTER ELEVATION SQUINT ANGLE (degrees)";SQEL
316 PRINT
318 PRINT "SELECT DESIRED MONOPULSE FUNCTION:"
32Ø PRINT
322 PRINT "        ENTER [SUM] FOR SUM FUNCTION"
324 PRINT "        ENTER [DELAZ] FOR AZIMUTH DIFFERENCE"
326 INPUT "        ENTER [DELEL] FOR ELEVATION DIFFERENCE";
    MONMOD$
332 LET AZOF(1) = SQAZ/2: LET ELOF(1) = SQEL/2
334 LET AZOF(2) = SQAZ/2: LET ELOF(2) = -SQEL/2
336 LET AZOF(3) = -SQAZ/2: LET ELOF(3) = SQEL/2
338 LET AZOF(4) = -SQAZ/2: LET ELOF(4) = -SQEL/2
375 LET ACC = Ø
38Ø IF FILE$ = "S" THEN GOTO 386 ELSE FOR K = 1 TO 6Ø
```

```
382 LET TC = (-15 + K*.5)

384 GOTO 392

386 PRINT

388 INPUT "ENTER ELEVATION OFFSET ANGLE, (degrees)";TC

392 FOR I = 1 TO 60

395 FOR KK = 1 TO 4

396 LET TA = (-15 - AZOF(KK) + I*.5)*DTR

397 LET TE = (TC - ELOF(KK))*DTR

398 GOSUB 1200:REM              ***** ANGULAR DISTORTION ******

400 GOSUB 1700:REM              ***** ELECTRONIC POINTING *****

402 GOSUB 1400:REM              ******* COMPOSITE ANGLE *******

404 GOSUB 1500:REM              ****** ROTATIONAL ANGLE *******

406 IF ABS(TH) <= U(NL) THEN GOTO 412

408 LET VG = 1E-10

410 GOTO 444

412 FOR J = 1 TO NL

414 IF L(J) < TH THEN IF TH <= U(J) THEN LET LB = J

416 NEXT J

418 LET L = -1*E10

420 LET L = L(LB)

422 LET U = U(LB)

424 LET M = M(LB)

426 LET E = E(LB)

428 LET N = LB

430 GOSUB 1000:REM                  ********* VOLTAGE GAIN ********

432 LET W = W(LB)

434 GOSUB 1100:REM              ****** TRIANGULAR SHAPING *****

436 LET NC = NC(LB)
```

```
438 LET FP = FP(LB)
440 LET PM = PM(LB)
442 LET CC = CC(LB)
444 FOR J = 1 TO CC
446 LET NLC(J) = NLCC(LB,J)
448 NEXT J
450 GOSUB 1600:REM              *****' RADIAL MODULATION ******
452 LET VG = VG*RM*SL
454 LET HG(KK) = VG
456 NEXT KK
458 LET ACC = ACC +1
460 IF MONMOD$ = "SUM" THEN LET GAIN(ACC) =(HG(1) + HG(2) +
    HG(3) + HG(4))/4
462 IF MONMOD$ = "DELAZ" THEN LET GAIN(ACC) =((HG(1) +
    HG(2)) - (HG(3) + HG(4)))/4
464 IF MONMOD$ = "DELEL" THEN LET GAIN(ACC) =((HG(1) +
    HG(3)) - (HG(2) + HG(4)))/4
466 IF GAIN(ACC) = 0 THEN LET GAIN(ACC) = 1E-10
467 PRINT TC,(I/2)-15,GAIN(ACC)
468 NEXT I
470 IF FILE$ = "M" THEN NEXT K
499 REM
500 REM ************ ORGANIZE FOR PLOT/FILING ************
501 REM
505 IF FILE$ = "S" THEN GOTO 525
509 CLS
510 INPUT "ENTER ELEVATION OFFSET (degrees)";ELE
512 PRINT
```

```
515 LET START = INT((ELE + 14.5)*120)

520 GOTO 530

525 LET START = 0

528 CLS

529 PRINT

530 PRINT "SELECT OUTPUT PLOT FORM"

535 INPUT "[0]= dBPG, [1] = dBVG, [2] = VG, [3] = PG";FP

539 REM

540 REM ********** SETUP PLOT/FILE OUTPUT **********

541 REM

542 LET GAIN(0) = 1E-10

543 LET STR = START

545 FOR I = 1 TO 61

547 LET II = I - 1

550 IF FP = 0 THEN LET GD(II) =
    20*(LOG(ABS(GAIN(STR+II)))/LOG(10))

555 IF FP = 1 THEN LET GD(II) =
    10*(LOG(ABS(GAIN(STR+II)))/LOG(10))

560 IF FP = 2 THEN LET GD(II) = GAIN(STR+II)

565 IF FP = 3 THEN LET GD(II) =
    ((GAIN(STR+II))^2)*SGN(GAIN(STR+II))

570 NEXT I

575 GOSUB 5000:REM              ********** GAIN PLOT **********

580 INPUT "TYPE [C] TO CONTINUE, [R] TO REPLOT";R$

585 IF R$ = "R" THEN GOTO 505

599 REM

600 REM ****** CALCULATE ATTENUATION DUE TO STEERING *******

601 REM
```

```
605 CLS

610 PRINT

615 PRINT "ENTER -3dB BEAMWIDTH, BW (IN DEGREES)"

616 PRINT "IF BWaz IS NOT EQUAL TO BWel THEN"

617 PRINT "ENTER SQRT(BWaz*BWel) FOR APPROXIMATE BW"

618 INPUT "OR ENTER [-99] TO VIEW PREVIOUS PLOT AGAIN";BWD

619 IF BWD = -99 THEN GOTO 575

620 LET BW = BWD*DTR

625 GOSUB 1800            ******** POINTING LOSS ********

630 PRINT

635 PRINT "MULTIPLICATIVE VOLTAGE GAIN COEFFICIENT"

640 PRINT "DUE TO ELECTRONIC POINTING =";GVS

665 PRINT

670 PRINT "TYPE [F] TO MAKE FILE, [R] TO RETURN, [E] TO
    EXIT"

675 INPUT "[P] TO RECALCULATE POINTING COEFFICIENT";D$

680 IF D$ = "R" THEN GOTO 35

685 IF D$ = "E" THEN GOTO 999

690 IF D$ = "P" THEN GOTO 600

700 REM ************* LOAD DATA FILE **************

701 REM

702 CLS

703 PRINT

704 PRINT "NOTE - FILE IS SAME FORM AS LAST PLOT!"

705 INPUT "ENTER [FILENAME] OR [N] TO CANCEL FILE";FLNM$

706 IF FLNM$ = "N" THEN GOTO 670

710 OPEN "O",#1,FLNM$

715 FOR I = 1 TO SIZE
```

```
720 IF FP = 0 THEN LET GDAT = 20*(LOG(ABS(GAIN(I)))/LOG(10))

725 IF FP = 1 THEN LET GDAT = 10*(LOG(ABS(GAIN(I)))/LOG(10))

730 IF FP = 2 THEN LET GDAT = GAIN(I)

735 IF FP = 3 THEN LET GDAT = ((GAIN(I))^2)*SGN(GAIN(I))

740 PRINT#1,GDAT

745 NEXT I

750 CLOSE#1

755 GOTO 670

999 END
```

A.3   EXAMPLE SIMULATION

The following is a demonstration of how the software listed in this appendix may be executed in order to create a desired antenna pattern.

Upon execution of the simulation, the user is first prompted to enter the number of lobes, up to a maximum of four, desired for the antenna pattern to be created:

```
ENTER DATA IN RESPONSE TO QUERIES.

ENTER NUMBER OF LOBES (<=4)? 3
```

Entering a value of 3, as shown, causes the simulation to prompt the user to enter parametric data in sequential order for each lobe, beginning with the main lobe (#1) and proceeding to the outermost sidelobe (#3):

```
***** ENTERING DATA FOR 3 LOBE(S). *****

FOR LOBE # 1 ENTER:
LOWER ANGULAR BOUNDARY (DEGREES)? -5
UPPER ANGULAR BOUNDARY (DEGREES)? 5
MAXIMUM RELATIVE VOLTAGE GAIN (dBVG)? 0
SHAPING COEFFICIENT (DIMENSIONLESS)? .055
TRIANGULAR SHAPE WEIGHTING? 0
NUMBER OF RADIAL MODULATION (RM) CYCLES? 0
```

```
FOR LOBE # 2 ENTER:
UPPER ANGULAR BOUNDARY (DEGREES)? 8
MAXIMUM RELATIVE VOLTAGE GAIN (dBVG)? -10
SHAPING COEFFICIENT (DIMENSIONLESS)? .045
TRIANGULAR SHAPE WEIGHTING? 0
NUMBER OF RADIAL MODULATION (RM) CYCLES? 4
POLARITY FLAG (RM)? 0
MODULATION PERCENTAGE (0 to 100)? 100
NUMBER OF NULL CYCLES (RM)(<=16)? 0
```

In the first two lobes, no radial modulation cycles were selected. In the third lobe, however, four radial modulation cycles were selected; thus, the simulation asks the user for some additional parameters for this lobe:

```
FOR LOBE # 3 ENTER:
UPPER ANGULAR BOUNDARY (DEGREES)? 11
MAXIMUM RELATIVE VOLTAGE GAIN (dBVG)? -15
SHAPING COEFFICIENT (DIMENSIONLESS)? .04
TRIANGULAR SHAPE WEIGHTING? 0
NUMBER OF RADIAL MODULATION (RM) CYCLES? 8
POLARITY FLAG (RM)? 0
MODULATION PERCENTAGE (0 to 100)? 100
NUMBER OF NULL CYCLES (RM)(<=16)? 4
NULL CYCLE NUMBER? 1
NULL CYCLE NUMBER? 3
NULL CYCLE NUMBER? 5
NULL CYCLE NUMBER? 7
```

After entering the lobe parameters, the user is prompted to enter parameters pertaining to the entire pattern:

```
***** SETTING UP ANGULAR DISTORTION *****

AZIMUTH DISTORTION COEFFICIENT (PER CENT)? 100
ELEVATION DISTORTION COEFFICIENT (PER CENT)? 100


*** SETTING UP PLANAR ARRAY POINTING ANGLES ***
        (ENTER 0s IF NOT PLANAR ARRAY)

AZIMUTH POINTING ANGLE? 30
ELEVATION POINTING ANGLE? 0
```

At this point, the user is permitted to review the parameters that have been entered, and to change them if desired. The first set displayed is the lobe parameters:

PRESENT SETUP IS:

1	2	3	n
-5	5	8	Ln
5	8	11	Un
0	-10	-15	Mn
.055	.045	.04	En
0	0	0	Wn
0	4	8	NCn
0	0	0	FPn
0	100	100	PMn
0	0	4	CCn
--	--	1	NLCn, 1
--	--	3	NLCn, 2
--	--	5	NLCn, 3
--	--	7	NLCn, 4

WANT TO MODIFY [VARIABLE] OR CONTINUE [C]? C

In this case, a [C] is entered, which permits us to move to the next screen. This screen permits us to review and modify the pattern parameters:

PRESENT SETUP IS:

DA = 100   DE = 100

PA = 30   PE = 0

WANT TO MODIFY [VARIABLE] OR CONTINUE [C]? PE
? 20

In this case, entering a [PE] informs the simulation that the user wishes to change the value of the elevation pointing angle, PE, which is currently set to 0°. Entering the desired value of 20 causes the screen to be repeated with the appropriate change in place:

PRESENT SETUP IS:

DA = 100   DE = 100

PA = 30   PE = 20

WANT TO MODIFY [VARIABLE] OR CONTINUE [C]? C

When the user is satisfied with the values, he or she may enter a [C] in order to move to the next screen, which offers a choice between a single antenna or a monopulse system:

```
ENTER [M] FOR MONOPULSE, [S] FOR SINGLE ANTENNA;? S

SELECT 3-D (MATRIX) OR 2-D (SLICE):
ENTER [M] FOR MATRIX, [S] FOR SLICE? S

ENTER ELEVATION OFFSET ANGLE, (degrees)? 0
```

If monopulse were selected, the user would be prompted to enter a squint angle. In this case, however, a single antenna was selected, so the user is required to select either a matrix or a slice. In this context, selection of the matrix option will permit calculation of a 60-point by 60-point matrix of gain values, representing a 30° azimuth by 30° elevation section of the pattern. Selection of the slice option will permit calculation of a 30° azimuth section at a selected constant elevation angle. For the example, the slice option is chosen at 0° elevation.

Following these entries, the gain data roll by as they are being calculated. This display is useful to the user desiring a quick look at the data as they are calculated. Following these calculations, the user is prompted to select the format of the graphical display:

```
SELECT OUTPUT PLOT FORM
[0]= dBPG, [1] = dBVG, [2] = VG, [3] = PG? 2
```

Now an antenna pattern will appear on the screen, and the user may choose to continue by entering a [C] or to replot the data by entering an [R], which will display the format selection menu shown above. When the user has viewed the graphical display sufficiently and enters the [C], the simulation moves to the following screen:

```
ENTER -3dB BEAMWIDTH, BW (IN DEGREES)
IF BWaz IS NOT EQUAL TO BWel THEN
ENTER SQRT(BWaz*BWel) FOR APPROXIMATE BW
OR ENTER [-99] TO VIEW PREVIOUS PLOT AGAIN? 6

MULTIPLICATIVE VOLTAGE GAIN COEFFICIENT
DUE TO ELECTRONIC POINTING = .7238647

TYPE [F] TO MAKE FILE, [R] TO RETURN, [E] TO EXIT
[P] TO RECALCULATE POINTING COEFFICIENT? E
```

The user must now enter the beamwidth in order to have the simulation calculate the voltage gain coefficient due to pointing. If the user decides to review the graphical display to ascertain the beamwidth, he or she can return to the format selection menu by entering a [−99]. Once the beamwidth is entered, the simulation calculates the pointing gain coefficient and then gives the user the option of returning [R] to the parameter modification screens, exiting [E], or making a data file [F] of the gain data calculated. The [R] option is convenient for making iterative changes in selected parameters without having to re-enter all the unchanged parameters. If the [F] option is chosen, the user is subsequently prompted to enter a file name. In this case, however, the [E] option is chosen, causing the simulation to terminate.

Appendix B
Radome Simulation Models

B.1   GEOMETRIC AND TRANSMISSION MODELS

The following listings are software implementations of the algorithms and functions derived in Part III. The programs, which are written in FORTRAN, are repetitions of those presented in Chapters 8 and 9.

```
        PROGRAM INCIDE
C
C       THIS PROGRAM GENERATES THE INTERSECTION POINT
C       AND ANGLE OF INCIDENCE FOR A GIVEN RADOME
        LENGTH ( C )
C
        WRITE(*,*) ' ENTER RADOME LENGTH (M) '
        READ(*,*) C
C
        OPEN( 1, FILE = 'RAD.DAT' )
C
        DO 10 I = 0, 90
              AZ = FLOAT( I ) / 57.296
              ZLK = 0.0
              XLK = COS( AZ )
              YLK = SIN( AZ )
              CALL RADOME( C, XLK, YLK, ZLK, XPR, YPR, ZPR,
              RAD )
              WRITE( 1, * ) XPR, ' , ' , YPR, ' , ' , RAD*57.296, ' , '
              ENDIF
   10   CONTINUE
```

```
C
      STOP
      END
C
      SUBROUTINE RADOME( C, XLK, YLK, ZLK, XPR, YPR, ZPR,
      RAD )
C
C     ***** SINE & COSINE OF LOOK ANGLE.
C
      CTHETA = XLK
      STHETA = SQRT( ABS( 1.0 - CTHETA * CTHETA ) )
C
C     ***** INTERSECTION POINT BETWEEN LOOK VECTOR AND
      RADOME.
C
      IF ( CTHETA.NE.0.0 ) GO TO 1
          XPR = 0.0
          GO TO 3
    1 IF ( STHETA.NE.0.0 ) GO TO 2
          XPR = C
          GO TO 3
    2 T = STHETA / CTHETA
      T = T * T
      X = ( -1.0 + SQRT( 1.0 + 4.0 * C * T ) ) / ( 2.0 * T )
      XPR = ABS( X )
    3 IF ( XPR.EQ.0.0 ) R = SQRT( C )
      IF ( XPR.EQ.0.0 ) GO TO 4
          R = XPR / CTHETA
    4 YPR = YLK * R
      ZPR = ZLK * R
C
C     ***** CALCULATE NORMAL TO RADOME SURFACE AT
      INTERSECTION.
C
      DMAG = SQRT( 1.0 + 4.0 * YPR * YPR + 4.0 * ZPR * ZPR )
      XN = 1.0 / DMAG
      YN = 2.0 * YPR / DMAG
      ZN = 2.0 * ZPR / DMAG
      CRAD = DOTPR( XLK,YLK,ZLK,XN,YN,ZN )
      SRAD = SQRT( ABS( 1.0 - CRAD * CRAD ) )
      RAD = ARCSIN( SRAD )
C
      RETURN
      END
```

```
        PROGRAM SMITH
C
C       THIS PROGRAM CALCULATES THE TRANSMISSION
C       COEFFICIENT FOR A MULTILAYERED RADOME.
C
        REAL WL,RAD,PI,TWOPI,DTOR,THE(10,2),THETA,
        LEN,COSI,COST
C
        COMPLEX ZO, J, RHOPARA, RHOPERP, Z_SPACE, T1, T2,
     $  CTANH, ZPHASE, MAT(10,5), ZT_PERP, ZT_PARA,
     $  ZL_PERP, ZL_PARA
C
        INTEGER I, N, K, ANGLE, KP1
C
C       INITIALIZE CONSTANTS
C
        PI     = 3.141592654
        TWOPI = 2.0 * PI
        DTOR   = PI / 180.0
C
C       INITIALIZE J = SQRT( -1 )
C
        J = ( 0.0 , 1.0 )
C
C       INITIALIZE FREE SPACE IMPEDANCE
C
        Z_SPACE = ( 0.0 , 376.7 )
C
        OPEN(1,FILE = 'PERP.TAU')
        OPEN(2,FILE = 'PARA.TAU')
C
C
        WRITE(*,*) 'INPUT NUMBER OF LAYERS   '
C
C       INPUT NUMBER OF LAYERS ( < 10 )
        READ(*,*) N
C
C       READ PARAMETERS
C
        MAT( N + 1 , 1 ) = (1.0, 0.0)
        MAT( N + 1 , 4 ) = Z_SPACE
        MAT( N + 1 , 2 ) = 0.0
```

```
C
C          REL. PERMITTIVITY OF MEDIA      MAT(X,1)
C          NORMAL DEPTH OF MEDIA           MAT(X,2)
C          WAVELENGTH IN MEDIA             MAT(X,3)
C          IMPEDANCE OF MEDIA              MAT(X,4)
C          PATH LENGTH IN MEDIA            MAT(X,5)
C          INCIDENT ANGLE COSINE           THE(X,1)
C          TRANSMITTED ANGLE COSINE        THE(X,2)
C
           WRITE(*,*) 'ENTER OPERATING WAVELENGTH ( M )  '
           READ(*,*) WL
C
           DO 100 I = 1,N
           WRITE (*,*) ' '
           WRITE(*,*) 'LAYER NUMBER ',I
           WRITE(*,*) 'INPUT;'
           WRITE(*,*) 'RELATIVE PERMITTIVITY '
           READ(*,*) MAT( I , 1 )
           WRITE(*,*) 'NORMAL LENGTH '
           READ(*,*)LEN
           MAT (I,2) = CMPLX (LEN,0.0)
C
   100     CONTINUE
C
C          THIS LOOP CALCULATES THE WAVELENGTH IN THE
C          MEDIA AND THE IMPEDANCE OF THE MEDIA
C
           DO 50 I = 1 , N
               MAT( I , 3 ) = WL / CSQRT( MAT( I , 1 ) )
               MAT( I , 4 ) = Z_SPACE / CSQRT( MAT( I , 1 ) )
   50      CONTINUE
C
C
C     ********************************
C     *                              *
C     *      BEGIN MAJOR LOOPS       *
C     *                              *
C     ********************************
C
           DO 1000 ANGLE = 0 , 90
C
           RAD = REAL( ANGLE ) * DTOR
```

```
C
C          BEGIN CALCULATIONS BY CALCULATING RAY PATH
           LENGTHS AND ANGLES
C
           DO 200 K = 1 , N + 1
           IF ( K .EQ. 1 ) THEN
               THE( K , 1 ) = COS( RAD )
               THETA = SIN( RAD ) / SQRT( CABS( MAT( 1 , 1 ) )
           ELSE
               THE( K , 1 ) = SQRT( 1.0 - THETA * THETA )
               THETA = SQRT( CABS( MAT(K - 1,1) / MAT(K,1) ) *
           THETA
           ENDIF
C
           THE( K, 2 ) = SQRT( 1.0 - THETA * THETA )
           MAT( K, 5 ) = MAT( K, 2 ) / THE( K, 2 )
C
      200  CONTINUE
C
C          NOW DEVELOP TRANSMISSION LINE EQUIVALENT
C
           DO 300 K = N , 1 , -1
C
               KP1 = K + 1
               COSI = THE( KP1, 1 )
               COST = THE( KP1, 2)
C
               IF ( K .EQ. N ) THEN
                   ZL_PERP = Z_SPACE
                   ZL_PARA = Z_SPACE
               ELSE
                   ZL_PERP = ZT_PERP
                   ZL_PARA = ZT_PARA
C              ENDIF
               ZO = MAT( K, 4 )
C
               ZPHASE = -J * TWOPI * MAT( K , 5 ) / MAT( K , 3 )
C
               IF ( CCOS( ZPHASE ) .EQ. 0.0 ) THEN
                   ZT_PERP = ZO * ZO * COST / ZL_PERP * COSI
                   ZT_PARA = ZO * ZO * COSI / ZL_PARA * COST
```

```
                 ELSE
                 ZT_PERP = ZO*( (ZL_PERP*COSI +
                                 ZO*COST*CTANH
                                 (ZPHASE)) /
                                 (ZO*COST + ZL_
                                 PERP*COSI*CTANH
        &                        (ZPHASE)) )
C

                 ZT_PARA = ZO*( (ZL_PARA*COST +
                                 ZO*COSI*CTANH
                                 (ZPHASE)) /
                                 (ZO*COSI + ZL_
                                 PARA*COST*CTANH
        &                        (ZPHASE)) )
                 ENDIF
C
   1000   CONTINUE
C
        COSI = THE( 1, 1 )
        COST = THE( 1, 2 )
C
        RHOPERP = ( ZT_PERP*COSI − Z_SPACE*COST )
        &          /( ZT_PERP*COSI + Z_SPACE*COST )
C
        RHOPARA = ( ZT_PARA*COST − Z_SPACE*COSI )
        &          /( ZT_PARA*COST + Z_SPACE*COSI )
C
        T1 = ( 1.0 − CABS( RHOPERP )**2 )
        T2 = ( 1.0 − CABS( RHOPARA )**2 )
C
        WRITE(1,*) CABS( T1 )
        WRITE(2,*) CABS( T2 )
C
   1000   CONTINUE
C
        CLOSE ( 1 )
        CLOSE ( 2 )
C
        STOP
        END
C
C
C          -------------------------------------------------------
C          COMPLEX HYPERBOLIC TANGENT
C          -------------------------------------------------------
```

```
C
          COMPLEX FUNCTION CTANH( U )
C
          COMPLEX U
          REAL ZR, ZI
C
          ZR = 2.0 * REAL( U )
          ZI = 2.0 * AIMAG( U )
C
          CTANH = CMPLX(SINH( ZR ), SIN( ZI )) /
     &            CMPLX(COSH( ZR ) + COS( ZI ), 0.0)
C
          RETURN
C
```

B.2 SUPPORT UTILITIES

The following mathematical utilities are those required to support the previously listed geometric and transmission programs for radome simulation.

```
C     ---------------------------------------------------------------
C                         SUBROUTINE "SPHREC"
C
C     THIS SUBROUTINE PERFORMS A SPHERICAL TO RECTANGULAR CONVERSION
C     FOR A RIGHT-HANDED COORDINATE SYSTEM WITH +Z DOWN. THETA IS
C     MEASURED UP FROM THE XY PLANE, AND PSI IS MEASURED FROM THE
C     XZ PLANE TOWARDS THE Y AXIS.
C
C     AUTHOR     : KURT E. HILDEBRANT
C     LAST REV.  : 10 / 30 / 85
C
C     INPUTS:  R          = R COMPONENT OF VECTOR.
C              RTHETA     = THETA COMPONENT OF VECTOR.
C              RPSI       = PSI COMPONENT OF VECTOR.
C              THETA      = ELEVATION ANGLE (RADIANS).
C              PSI        = AZIMUTH ANGLE (RADIANS).
C
C     OUTPUTS: X,Y,Z      = VECTOR COMPONENTS (RECTANGULAR).
```

```
C      ----------------------------------------------------------------
C
       SUBROUTINE SPHREC( R,RTHETA,RPSI,THETA,PSI,X,Y,Z )
C
C      ***** GET ANGLE SINES AND COSINES.
C
       CTHETA = COS( THETA )
       STHETA = SIN( THETA )
       CPSI   = COS( PSI )
       SPSI   = SIN( PSI )
C
C      ***** CALCULATE RECTANGULAR COMPONENTS.
C
       X =  R * CTHETA * CPSI - RTHETA * STHETA * CPSI - RPSI * SPSI
       Y =  R * CTHETA * SPSI - RTHETA * STHETA * SPSI + RPSI * CPSI
       Z = -R * STHETA        - RTHETA * CTHETA
       RETURN
       END
C
C      ----------------------------------------------------------------
C                        SUBROUTINE "RECSPH"
C
C      THIS SUBROUTINE PERFORMS A RECTANGULAR TO SPHERICAL CONVERSION
C      FOR A RIGHT-HANDED COORDINATE SYSTEM WITH +Z DOWN. THETA IS
C        MEASURED UP FROM THE XY PLANE, AND PSI IS MEASURED FROM THE
C        XZ PLANE TOWARDS THE Y AXIS.
C
C      AUTHOR     : KURT E. HILDEBRANT
C      LAST REV.  : 10 / 30 / 85
C
C      INPUTS:  X,Y,Z    = RECTANGULAR COMPONENTS.
C               THETA    = ELEVATION ANGLE (RADIANS).
C               PSI      = AZIMUTH ANGLE (RADIANS).
```

```
C
C      OUTPUTS: R           = R COMPONENT.
C               RTHETA      = ELEVATION COMPONENT.
C               RPSI        = AZIMUTH COMPONENT.
C
C      ------------------------------------------------------------------
C
       SUBROUTINE RECSPH( X,Y,Z,THETA,PSI,R,RTHETA,RPSI )
C
C      ***** GET ANGLE SINES AND COSINES.
C
       CTHETA = COS( THETA )
       STHETA = SIN( THETA )
       CPSI   = COS( PSI )
       SPSI   = SIN( PSI )
C
C      ***** CALCULATE SPHERICAL COMPONENTS.
C
       R      = X * CTHETA * CPSI + Y * CTHETA * SPSI - Z * STHETA
       RTHETA = X * STHETA * CPSI - Y * STHETA * SPSI - Z * CTHETA
       RPSI   = -X * SPSI          + Y * CPSI
       RETURN
       END
C
C      ------------------------------------------------------------------
C                          SUBROUTINE "CROSSP"
C
C      THIS SUBROUTINE CALCULATES THE VECTOR (CROSS) PRODUCT OF THE
C      TWO INPUT VECTORS.
C
C      AUTHOR     : KURT E. HILDEBRANT
C      LAST REV.  : 10 / 30 / 85
C
```

```
C      INPUTS:  X1,Y1,Z1 = VECTOR 1 COMPONENTS.

C               X2,Y2,Z2 = VECTOR 2 COMPONENTS.

C

C      OUTPUTS: X3,Y3,Z3 = CROSS PRODUCT COMPONENTS.

C      -------------------------------------------------------------------

C

       SUBROUTINE CROSSP( X1,Y1,Z1,X2,Y2,Z2,X3,Y3,Z3 )

C

       X3 = Y1 * Z2 - Z1 * Y2

       Y3 = Z1 * X2 - X1 * Z2

       Z3 = X1 * Y2 - Y1 * X2

       RETURN

       END

C

C      -------------------------------------------------------------------

C                       SUBROUTINE "FEULER"

C

C      THIS SUBROUTINE TRANSFORMS VECTOR COMPONENTS FROM SYSTEM 1 INTO

C        SYSTEM 2 WHERE SYSTEM 1 HAS EULER ANGLES THETA, PSI, AND PHI

C        W.R.T. SYSTEM 2. BOTH SYSTEMS ARE RIGHT-HANDED WITH +Z DOWN.

C

C      AUTHOR     : KURT E. HILDEBRANT

C      LAST REV.  : 10 / 30 / 85

C

C      INPUTS:  X1,Y1,Z1  = COMPONENTS IN SYSTEM 1.

C               THETA     = ELEVATION ANGLE OF 1 W.R.T. 2.

C               PSI       = AZIMUTH ANGLE OF 1 W.R.T. 2.

C               PHI       = ROLL ANGLE OF 1 W.R.T. 2.

C

C      OUTPUTS: X2,Y2,Z2  = COMPONENTS IN SYSTEM 2.

C      -------------------------------------------------------------------

C

       SUBROUTINE FEULER( X1,Y1,Z1,THETA,PSI,PHI,X2,Y2,Z2 )
```

```
C

      Y  =  Y1 * COS( PHI )    - Z1 * SIN( PHI )

      Z  =  Y1 * SIN( PHI )    + Z1 * COS( PHI )

      X  =  X1 * COS( THETA ) +  Z * SIN( THETA )

      X2 =   X * COS( PSI )    -  Y * SIN( PSI )

      Y2 =   X * SIN( PSI )    +  Y * COS( PSI )

      Z2 = -X1 * SIN( THETA ) +  Z * COS( THETA )

C

      RETURN

      END

C

C     ------------------------------------------------------------------

C                        SUBROUTINE "REULER"

C

C     THIS SUBROUTINE TRANSFORMS VECTOR COMPONENTS FROM SYSTEM 2 INTO

C     SYSTEM 1 WHERE SYSTEM 1 HAS EULER ANGLES THETA, PSI, AND PHI

C     W.R.T. SYSTEM 2. BOTH SYSTEMS ARE RIGHT-HANDED WITH +Z DOWN.

C

C     AUTHOR     : KURT E. HILDEBRANT

C     LAST REV.  : 10 / 30 / 85

C

C     INPUTS:  X2,Y2,Z2  = COMPONENTS IN SYSTEM 2.

C              THETA     = ELEVATION ANGLE OF 1 W.R.T. 2.

C              PSI       = AZIMUTH ANGLE OF 1 W.R.T. 2.

C              PHI       = ROLL ANGLE OF 1 W.R.T. 2.

C

C     OUTPUTS: X1,Y1,Z1  = COMPONENTS IN SYSTEM 1.

C     ------------------------------------------------------------------

C

      SUBROUTINE REULER( X2,Y2,Z2,THETA,PSI,PHI,X1,Y1,Z1 )

C

      X  =  X2 * COS( PSI )    + Y2 * SIN( PSI )

      Y  = -X2 * SIN( PSI )    + Y2 * COS( PSI )
```

```
      Z  =   X * SIN( THETA ) + Z2 * COS( THETA )
      X1 =   X * COS( THETA ) - Z2 * SIN( THETA )
      Y1 =   Y * COS( PHI )   + Z * SIN( PHI )
      Z1 =  -Y * SIN( PHI )   + Z * COS( PHI )
C

      RETURN
      END
C
C    ----------------------------------------------------------------
C                         SUBROUTINE "NORMAL"
C
C    THIS SUBROUTINE CALCULATES THE UNIT VECTORS PARALLEL AND
C     PERPENDICULAR TO THE PLANE DEFINED BY UNIT LOOK VECTOR L
C     AND UNIT SURFACE NORMAL N.
C
C    AUTHOR    : KURT E. HILDEBRANT
C    LAST REV. : 10 / 30 / 85
C
C    INPUTS:  XL,YL,ZL = UNIT LOOK VECTOR COMPONENTS.
C             XN,YN,ZN = UNIT SURFACE NORMAL COMPONENTS.
C
C    OUTPUTS: VX,VY,VZ = VERTICAL (PARALLEL) UNIT VECTOR COMPONENTS.
C             HX,HY,HZ = HORIZONTAL (PERPENDICULAR) COMPONENTS.
C    ----------------------------------------------------------------
C
      SUBROUTINE NORMAL( XL,YL,ZL,XN,YN,ZN,VX,VY,VZ,HX,HY,HZ )
C
C    ***** L X N.
C
      CALL CROSSP( XL,YL,ZL,XN,YN,ZN,XLCN,YLCN,ZLCN )
C
C    ***** L * N = COS( THETA ).
```

```
C
      CTHETA = DOTPR( XL,YL,ZL,XN,YN,ZN )
      STHETA = SQRT( ABS( 1.0 - CTHETA * CTHETA ) )
C
C     ***** HORZ = L X N / SIN( THETA ).
C
      HX = XLCN / STHETA
      HY = YLCN / STHETA
      HZ = ZLCN / STHETA
C
C     ***** VERT = H X L.
C
      CALL CROSSP( HX,HY,HZ,XL,YL,ZL,VX,VY,VZ )
      RETURN
      END
C
C     ----------------------------------------------------------------
C                          SUBROUTINE "UNITV"
C
C     THIS SUBROUTINE CALCULATES THE MAGNITUDE OF THE INPUT VECTOR
C     AND THE COMPONENTS OF THE CORRESPONDING UNIT VECTOR.
C
C     AUTHOR     : KURT E. HILDEBRANT
C     LAST REV.  : 10 / 30 / 85
C
C     INPUTS:  X,Y,Z    = VECTOR COMPONENTS.
C
C     OUTPUTS: XU,YU,ZU = UNIT VECTOR COMPONENTS.
C              VMAG     = INPUT VECTOR MAGNITUDE.
C     ----------------------------------------------------------------
C
      SUBROUTINE UNITV( X,Y,Z,XU,YU,ZU,VMAG )
C
```

```
      XU = 0.0

      YU = 0.0

      ZU = 0.0

      VMAG = SQRT( X * X + Y * Y + Z * Z )

      IF ( VMAG .EQ. 0.0 ) GO TO 1

      XU   = X / VMAG

      YU   = Y / VMAG

      ZU   = Z / VMAG

   1  CONTINUE

      RETURN

      END
C
C
C     ----------------------------------------------------------------
C
C                         SUBROUTINE "DIRCOS"
C
C     THIS SUBROUTINE RETURNS THE DIRECTION COSINES FOR THE INPUT
C       AZIMUTH AND ELEVATION.
C
C     AUTHOR      : DOUG GROVE
C     LAST REV.   : 12 / 07 / 86
C
C     INPUTS : AZ = AZIMUTH ( RAD )
C              EL = ELEVATION( RAD )
C              Y, Z = COMPONENTS OF UNIT VECTOR
C
C     ----------------------------------------------------------------
C
      SUBROUTINE DIRCOS( AZ, EL, Y, Z )
C
      REAL DWNRNG
C
C     +Z IS UP, +X IS OUT THE NOSE, +Y IS OUT THE RIGHT WING
C
      Z = -SIN( EL )
```

```
      DWNRNG = COS( EL )
      Y = DWNRNG * SIN( AZ )
C
      RETURN
      END
C
C     ----------------------------------------------------------
C                         SUBROUTINE "SINX"
C
C     THIS IS THE SIN( X ) / X ROUTINE FROM FAST ARRAY
C
C     AUTHOR    : DOUG GROVE
C     LAST REV. : 12 / 07 / 86
C
C     INPUTS    : Y, Z DIRECTION COSINES
C                 LENGTH = RADOME DIAMETER IN METERS
C                 LAMBDA = WAVELENGTH
C     OUTPUTS   : GAIN SINC GAIN
C
C     ----------------------------------------------------------
C
      SUBROUTINE SINX( Y, Z, RLENGT, RLAMBD, GAIN )
C
      REAL X
C
      X = SQRT( Y*Y + Z*Z )
      X = 3.14159265 * RLENGT * X / RLAMBD
      IF ( X .EQ. 0.0 ) THEN
         GAIN = 1.0
      ELSE
         GAIN = SIN( X ) / X
      ENDIF
C
```

```
      RETURN
      END
C
C     -------------------------------------------------------------------
C                        FUNCTION "ARCTAN"
C
C     THIS FUNCTION CALL RETURNS ARCTAN( Y / X ) IN THE RANGE +/- PI.
C       ANGLES ARE MEASURED FROM THE X-AXIS, POSITIVE CCW.
C
C     AUTHOR     : KURT E. HILDEBRANT
C     LAST REV.  : 11 / 06 / 85
C     -------------------------------------------------------------------
C
      REAL FUNCTION ARCTAN( Y,X )
C
      PI  = 3.141592654
      HPI = PI / 2.0
      X1  = ABS( X )
      Y1  = ABS( Y )
      IF ( Y ) 10,20,30
  10  IF ( X ) 6,7,8
  20  IF ( X ) 5,1,1
  30  IF ( X ) 4,3,2
C
   1  ARCTAN = 0.0
      RETURN
   2  ARCTAN = ATAN( Y1 / X1 )
      RETURN
   3  ARCTAN = HPI
      RETURN
   4  ARCTAN = PI - ATAN( Y1 / X1 )
      RETURN
```

```
5     ARCTAN = PI
      RETURN
6     ARCTAN = ATAN( Y1 / X1 ) - PI
      RETURN
7     ARCTAN = -HPI
      RETURN
8     ARCTAN = -ATAN( Y1 / X1 )
      RETURN
      END
C
C     ----------------------------------------------------------------
C                          FUNCTION "DOTPR"
C
C     THIS FUNCTION CALL RETURNS THE SCALAR (DOT) PRODUCT OF THE TWO
C      INPUT VECTORS.
C
C     AUTHOR     : KURT E. HILDEBRANT
C
C     ----------------------------------------------------------------
C                          FUNCTION "ARCSIN"
C
C     THIS FUNCTION CALL RETURNS ASIN(X) AND TRAPS |X| > 1.
C
C     AUTHOR     : KURT E. HILDEBRANT
C     LAST REV.  : 12 / 07 / 86 D. GROVE
C     ----------------------------------------------------------------
C
      REAL FUNCTION ARCSIN( X )
C
      XX = X
      IF( ABS( XX ) .GT. 1.0 ) XX = ABS( XX ) / XX
      ARCSIN = ASIN( XX )
```

```
      RETURN
      END
C
C     ----------------------------
C      COMPLEX HYPERBOLIC TANGENT
C     ----------------------------
C
      COMPLEX FUNCTION CTANH( U )
C
      COMPLEX U
      REAL ZR, ZI
C
C     LAST REV.  : 10 / 30 / 85
C
C     INPUTS:  X1,Y1,Z1 = VECTOR 1 COMPONENTS.
C              X2,Y2,Z2 = VECTOR 2 COMPONENTS.
C     ----------------------------------------------------------------
C
      REAL FUNCTION DOTPR( X1,Y1,Z1,X2,Y2,Z2 )
C
      DOTPR = ( X1 * X2 ) + ( Y1 * Y2 ) + ( Z1 * Z2 )
      RETURN
      END
C
C     ----------------------------------------------------------------
C                          FUNCTION "ARCCOS"
C
C     THIS FUNCTION CALL RETURNS ACOS(X) AND TRAPS ¦X¦ > 1.
C
C     AUTHOR     : KURT E. HILDEBRANT
C     LAST REV.  : 12 / 07 / 86 D. GROVE
```

```
C      --------------------------------------------------------------
C
       REAL FUNCTION ARCCOS( X )
C
       XX = X
       IF( ABS( XX ) .GT. 1.0 ) XX = ABS( XX ) / XX
       ARCCOS = ACOS( XX )
       RETURN
       END
       ZR = 2.0 * REAL( U )
       ZI = 2.0 * IMAG( U )
C
       CTANH = CMPLX(SINH( ZR ), SIN( ZI )) /
     &         CMPLX(COSH( ZR ) + COS( ZI ), 0.0)
C
       RETURN
       END
```

Index